MORE TA

WORC.

ROYAL

INFIRMARY

MIRIAM HARVEY
S.R.N.

WORCESTERSHIRE INDUSTRIAL
ARCHAEOLOGY AND LOCAL HISTORY
SOCIETY

More Tales from Worcester Royal Infirmary

Miriam Harvey

Published by Aspect Design 2015
Malvern, Worcestershire, United Kingdom
On behalf of
Worcestershire Industrial Archaeology and Local History Society (WIALHS)
www.worcester-wia.co.uk

Printed by Aspect Design
89 Newtown Road, Malvern, Worcs. WR14 1PD
United Kingdom
Tel: 01684 561567
E-mail: books@aspect-design.net
Website: www.aspect-design.net

TABLE OF CONTENTS

INTRODUCTION

Soon after publishing my book, 'Tales from Worcester Royal Infirmary', I realised that there must be many more 'tales' to tell, which should have been included, so here goes with a few more.

The hospital way of life of the 1950s has completely vanished. It was quite literally a different world to what we know today; an enclosed world of traditions, a hierarchy with unquestioned obedience. Because most of us 'lived in' at that time, our whole lives revolved round the hospital, the nurses home and the people living there. It seemed to me that someone needed to record these tales of that secluded life, when we were all in it together, all in the same boat.

So I have included some tales of individuals, living eventful and interesting lives, but also some personal reminiscences. My memories maybe not identical to those of others but as far as I can remember these are true accounts of life in the 1950s Worcester Royal Infirmary.

Looking back over the centuries I realise how much the various hospitals and alms-houses have depended on the goodwill and boundless generosity of many ordinary people in addition to the more wealthy citizens. As today, people have always been willing to give to a good cause.

I hope my colleagues will enjoy these tales and will share the happy memories of life-long friendships. I have always been very proud to have trained and worked at the WRI during the 1950s, which is regarded as the golden age of nursing when we received such excellent training and had wonderful role models in the senior staff and Matron was in charge!

MY EARLY YEARS

As far as I can remember since the age of about five or six, I have always wanted to be a Nurse. I have no idea where the idea came from as I had no contact with friends or relations who were nurses. But this idea was fixed in my head. My Mother made me a Nurses Uniform out of an old sheet, I spent many hours bandaging teddies and dolls and giving them spoonfuls of 'medicine'.

NURSE RECRUITMENT IN THE 1950S - *SHOWING HOW GLAMOROUS NURSING WAS!*

The day war broke out we were on holiday in Towyn, Wales. My Father left us that day, volunteering to join the Fleet Air Arm to offer his services as a Radio Telegraphy Operator, which was his hobby. Our home was in Kings Norton, Birmingham, but my father, realizing that there was likely to be bombing there, arranged for us to move down to Cornwall to married quarters to be near him, as he was stationed at St. Evel, part of St Morgan Air Base. Then we moved to a cottage in Treyarnon Bay. This is where my games of playing 'nurses' started. I would line up all the dolls along the old stone wall in the garden. The beds were made of cardboard boxes and dusters for the bed clothes. My little brother Paul was also a 'patient', but I could never get him to lie down!

I remember leaving our home on a cold and frosty November morning, travelling by train down to St. Merryn, where the married quarters were. We didn't like it much, but I started to attend the village school, which was very enjoyable. Each day we stood round an iron stove in the centre of the room and sang, "There'll always be an England" and "For those in peril on the sea" – both very moving. My Mother made me a 'Pasty' every day for lunch, but the part I loved most was reading. My Mother read lots of books to my younger brother Paul and I, and I couldn't wait to learn to read. Maybe I read something about Nursing, I don't know, but the idea of becoming a nurse never left me.

We spent the war years in Treyarnon Bay and then returned to Birmingham in 1945. I eventually passed my 11 plus exam and was fortunate to attend Holly Lodge Grammar School where I studied the Sciences, including physiology, and then in the Sixth form – Part 1 of the Nursing Pre-lim Exam. Our Chemistry Mistress Miss Jones was aware that I wanted to train as a Nurse and did everything she could to help and encourage me. During the 1940s and 1950s there was a major recruitment drive to encourage girls to enter the nursing profession.

I decided I didn't want to go to one of the big teaching Hospitals but chose Worcester Royal Infirmary as it had an excellent reputation. The Nursing Council recommended it as a training school and I had seen the beautiful building on a visit to Worcester a couple of years previously, and had fallen in love with it. I came for an interview with Matron Healey and she was very warm and welcoming, so I was accepted for Training in August 1954.

While waiting to start my Training I worked as a Volunteer at St. Chad's Hospital on the Hagley Road in Birmingham. As they did not provide any uniform, my Mother again made me one out of an old sheet. I don't think I learnt much at St Chads except – how to make 'Egg and Mayonnaise Sandwiches' which the patients had every day for their tea!

When the time came to start my training I was really excited to be starting out on this adventure. I joined another 20 girls all of a similar age to myself who would work together in the classroom during the following three years, but work individually gaining experience in all the different Wards and Departments throughout the Hospital.

However, first came the Preliminary Training School (P.T.S.) which tested our suitability and aptitude for training to be a Nurse. This included basic tasks – bed making, bed bathing, feeding patients etc., as well as learning Anatomy and Physiology, Hygiene, Dietetics etc. As I had already passed Part 1, I was able to spend more time on the Wards. After three months we were assessed and those who passed commenced their training proper. We had been issued with white shapeless starched dresses, but now we were given 3 made to measure grey cotton dresses, 14 white aprons, 5 stiff white collars, 5 plain white caps, 5 pairs of cuffs and 2 stiff white belts.

The first time I put my proper Uniform on I was extremely proud to think I was starting to live my dream of becoming a Nurse. I vowed I would do my very best to be a good Nurse, no matter how difficult it may be.

MY FRIEND INGE

Inge was sophisticated – tall, slim and striking looking – not pretty in the conventional way.

She came over from Berlin to Worcester to train as a nurse at Worcester Royal Infirmary in 1954, and we became friends almost straight away. Her father was German and her mother was Swedish, from Uppsala, so she spoke both languages – her English was perfect as well.

But it wasn't until we shared a flat nearing the end of our third year of training that I really got to know her. She used to laugh at me, calling me 'typically English' – and I was never sure whether that was a compliment or not! I was shy and not at all worldly wise as she was. Much to my shock, Inge, with her Swedish lack of inhibitions, after work used to wander around the flat completely naked. If friends called to see us I had to urge her to put some clothes on before we let them in!

Another habit was her smoking. Each pay-day, she would buy a month's supply of cigarettes, in bulk and she finally persuaded me to start smoking, showing me how to inhale. It was thirty years later that I finally gave up the habit. Inge

INGE LUBBERMEIR

5

was a very friendly person and I always enjoyed her company; we kept the flat clean and tidy as we saw eye to eye over the domestic arrangements.

We had to share a bathroom with a very nice girl in the next flat, but that was OK too, as we all became really good friends, and the girl in the next flat, Margaret, took Inge's place when Inge left for the USA, after we had finished our training.

The flat was in Barbourne, only fifteen minutes' walk from the Hospital. So we often used to walk along the racecourse to work in the mornings at 7.00am, meeting and greeting the same people each day. One elderly man who regularly said, "Good Morning" to me, one day stopped me and said he wanted to run away with me, I ran in the other direction! Apparently he was a horse doctor, not a Vet, and kept some stables in Diglis and he gave me some of his old medical books, I never knew his name.

The furnishings in the flat were quite unusual, it was just one large room, and the cooker, sink and fridge all folded away inside a long cupboard, and the table 'unfolded' to make a double bed – very cleverly disguised. Of course we had several parties there, and that's where I first drank alcohol. Gin and It, or Italian Vermouth was my first downfall – I drank so much of it I was violently sick, and have not touched that particular combination since.

On my 21st Birthday we decided to have a party, but all we could afford was one bottle of Gin, we had no money for proper food, so we ended up having 'pea-sandwiches' – and dancing round the room to Beethoven's 5th Symphony played on my new record player, a gift from my parents.

After taking our 'finals' Inge decided she would like to be an Air Hostess, which was considered a very glamorous job. She applied and was accepted with Pan American Airlines, known as Pan Am. Off she went to New York and quickly took to the job as Air Hostess flying all over the world.

A few months later, Inge came back to the Infirmary for prize-giving day, and brought with her a Film Crew, who were filming her visit for a New York Magazine. So we were all filmed all day at the Infirmary and at the flat. Inge received a prize that day, and so did I and we received our Hospital Badges made of Silver, with the Worcester coat of Arms, which we proudly wore.

Inge went back to New York and we didn't meet for another 35 years, although we regularly exchanged letters. After a few years with Pan Am, she worked for an eminent Surgeon as his Nurse and private assistant, and eventually married him. He was a Partner at the famous "Doctor's Hospital" in Manhattan, and had a sign in his car which allowed him to park anywhere he liked! Can you imagine? When my husband and I visited them we were very impressed with this concession to park in Manhattan. Inge's husband specialised in breast cancer and he had written several books on the subject, for which Inge had done much of the research.

Inge lived in the Upper East Side, a very up-market area, in a very tall apartment building on the 20th floor. At night the view was spectacular, with all the lights from many famous buildings, including the 'Twin Towers', the Empire State Building and the Chrysler Tower.

Inge's husband lived in a separate building. He was considerably older than Inge, but all the same we were really shocked to learn, only a few days after our visit that he suddenly dropped dead.

Inge sold up both apartments and moved to Miami, and I never saw or heard from her again. I was very sorry to have lost contact with Inge, she came over to stay with us only once and we still got on well together.

MARY DEVEREUX – THE PRETTIEST NURSE

Mary was tall, redheaded and had certainly kissed the Blarney Stone – she could charm the birds out of the trees and a great story teller.

Born in a small town in West Cork, the second of eight children, she was only seventeen when she travelled alone to Worcester, taking the ferry to Cardiff then the train to Worcester. Never having been out of Dunmanway before it was quite an adventure and she was very excited to be starting a new life as a Student Nurse.

Mary's mother's best friend worked as an Auxiliary at Ronkswood Hospital in Worcester, so it was thought she could keep a motherly eye on Mary, if she came to Worcester Royal Infirmary to do her training.

Coming from a large Roman Catholic family Mary was used to sharing everything, her bed and bedroom, and even the tin bath which was brought into the kitchen was shared, one night for the four girls and another for the four boys.

So it was a great luxury to find she not only had her own bed, but a bedroom to herself, which was cleaned for her and her bed made every day. The Nurses Home was palatial, with polished parquet floors, central heating and bathrooms on every corridor. It was sheer bliss on her afternoon off to have a bath full of warm scented water, filled right to the top, a far cry from the old tin-bath in the kitchen.

Because she was under 18, the usual age to start Nurses Training, Mary worked as a pre-nursing student on Bates Med, the children's Medical Ward. Having been used to caring for her younger brothers and sisters at home, she found she adapted very well to caring for young patients.

The following June, Mary started in the Preliminary Training School (PTS) which is a 3-month assessment and a very basic instruction before commencing Training as a Nurse. There were only six people in Mary's PTS, three of whom failed the preliminary exams and left. One of the remainder - Prue Henderson who passed and went on to do her training and Sonia Jones, a slightly more mature girl aged 23, who was so terrified of Sister Martin, a rather formidable Sister in charge of Rushout Ward, that she ran away, doing a midnight flit. Mary being the only person she told about how she felt.

Mary wrote regularly to her own family but did not feel homesick. On her days off she enjoyed going to the Cadena Café on the High Street, quite a novelty as there were no Coffee bars in her home town. She also frequented the Oyster Bar. Daily life in Worcester was very different from her home town, Mary thought it very weird that very few people seemed to go to church each Sunday.

During her training, which she really enjoyed caring for all her patients, she met and immediately fell in love with Neil Taylor, he was a patient suffering from Malaria, Neil was the only child of Christine Taylor, licensee of the 'Grandstand Hotel' on Worcester Racecourse (Pitchcroft) which is very close to the Infirmary. He would sometimes call for Mary at the Nurses Home riding his horse, the Nurses all thought how romantic it was. They became engaged at Easter 1956, planning to marry the following January. In July 1956 Neil and Mary went to Ireland to meet the family.

Towards the end of her training, Mary rented a flat in Hylton Road which she shared with Anna James and Prue Henderson. It was a short walk to the Hospital and had lovely views over the river and racecourse. Mary had discovered that she was pregnant and both families were delighted. In November Mary heard she had passed her State and Hospital final exams, so everything was looking rosy, Neil and Mary were on top of the World.

Then tragedy struck and the world came tumbling down around Mary's head. In late November, Neil had visited Mary in her flat and left at approximately 10.45pm. Struggling to get his car started, which was parked outside, a car travelling down towards Worcester at speed, crashed into Neil and his car, killing Neil instantly.

Unaware of what had happened Mary went to bed, then the following morning, when Neil did not arrive to take her to work, Mary ran down Hylton Road, across Worcester bridge to the Hospital. She was met by Night Sister who took her to Matron Healey. The tragic news was broken to Mary who collapsed on hearing of the terrible accident. She was inconsolable, even her young sister Anne could not comfort her. Anne had come over from Ireland recently to commence her training. Mary never got over the shock of this tragedy. She spent Christmas at home in Ireland and then came back to live with Neil's mother Christine at the 'Grandstand'.

Mary continued working on Bates Surgical children's ward, but started showing symptoms of Toxaemia of Pregnancy. An X-ray showed she was expecting twins. Mr A.T. Marshall, consultant obstetrician, visited her at the 'Grandstand' – she was rushed up to Ronkswood Maternity Unit where she went into premature /labour at 36 weeks. The first baby, a boy suffered cerebral irritation and died three days later. The other baby a girl named Gail was also very poorly, but she survived, a lovely golden haired blue eyed child.

As it was considered unsuitable for Gail to live at the 'Grandstand', Mary and baby went to live in London Road, where she shared a house with her friend Pauline Kelly. The two girls shared baby-sitting duties and working shifts as Industrial Nurses at the Metal Box Co. In 1960 Mary's parents had moved from Ireland to live in Worcester where they stayed for approx. 12 years.

In 1963 the film "Doctor in Distress" was showing at the Gaumont Cinema in Worcester and as part of the publicity the local Evening Newspaper arranged a "Prettiest Nurse" competition, which was won by Mary. The prize, some vouchers presented by the Mayor Hilda Lettice.

You would have thought Mary had already experienced more than her fair share of tragedy, but no. Two years later she married John Devereux, a man 13 years older! He turned out to be totally unreasonable and as soon as she could she divorced John Devereux when their daughter Jane was five years old.

Mary went to work at the Eye Hospital, Barbourne Road which she really loved, staying for 17½ years gaining her Ophthalmic Nursing Diploma at Moorfields in London.

1979 Seeking a change, Mary noticed an advertisement in the Nursing Times for an exciting post at a brand new Hospital in Abu Dhabi. Mary's daughters were both grown up by now, Gail was 22 and had trained as a Nurse at Powick Psychiatric Hospital and Jane was now 19 years old. So Mary applied for and got the job, although neither she nor the family knew where Abu Dhabi was?

Abu Dhabi is the wealthiest place in the Arab Emirates, owning 95% of the oil. A major development was taking place of roads, hotels and a huge Hospital for the Army, Navy and Air force called Sheik Zayed Military Hospital. The first thing Mary noticed of course was the overpowering heat, but of course air conditioning was installed in the Hospital. After two months she was promoted to Assistant Matron. There were new people arriving all the time from overseas.

Then came the 1st Gulf War which delayed her coming home for Christmas, but her daughters were allowed to visit. Then she left Abu Dhabi and came home to be with her daughters for two years.

In 1981 Mary worked with Topsy Davis on the District for Dr. Roma's practice, then later in the year went to work in Ireland for the first time as Matron of the Eye, Ear, Nose and Throat Hospital in Cork City.

It was very old fashioned and it rained every day, so she only stuck it for one year and one day.

Early in 1983 she went to Riyadh where she helped to commission a small satellite Hospital, opened by the Crown Prince of Saudi Arabia – Sheik Salman bin Abdul-Aziz. 77 Philippine Nurses came to work at the Hospital, they were open and friendly. The hospital was very busy, the 'mother' Hospital was enormous with 1,500 Philippine Nurses and 600 Korean Nurses who had their own Korean Matron. During her time in Abu Dhabi and Riyadh, Mary became very fond of the Arabic people who all treated her very well.

In 1986 Mary came back to work at the Eye Hospital again and to Moorfield where she did a 13-week intensive Ophthalmic Theatre course. Mary was now living alone as both daughters had their own homes, so her next stop was Jeddah at the National Guard Hospital for one year, where she worked on a large busy miscellaneous unit with 48 beds – including general surgery, dentistry and also a private wing. When she came back Mary was hoping to work at Malvern but suffered a ruptured gastric Ulcer while awaiting interview.

Having recovered, in 1990 she went to work in San Francisco. Here she worked in a Private Clinic where minor surgery was carried out. She had her 'Green Card' which allowed her to work legally and there was an amnesty for Irish people. She thought San Francisco was beautiful and loved working there.

Coming back to England a couple of years later she worked in Occupational Health for the British Nursing Agency. Mary worked at 'Evesham Foods' who made pastries for M&S, 'Garringtons' in Bromsgrove and 'Kay's Catalogue' in the Tything in Worcester. She also worked for the 'Royal National School for the Blind' in Hereford, which had 250 pupils and where she often had to sleep overnight.

In 1997 Mary met and became engaged to Ralph Slazenger, a wealthy sports businessman, who had an estate in Ireland but lived on the Isle of Man. She changed her mind in the end and didn't fancy living overseas.

For several years, since 1993 Mary has suffered 'dizzy spells'. It happened if she bent down suddenly but always subsided after a few seconds. She also suffered Hypertension and was seen by Consultant Dr. Scrivens. In 2001 she was referred to the Nuffield Hospital, and after a 'tilt test' was diagnosed as having Supra Ventricular Tachycardia. She was prescribed 'satalol' and 'bendroflurazide' which caused serious side-effects which were ignored by her doctors.

In November 2001 – having stayed overnight at the Blind College, she was feeling unwell, at 8am she boiled the kettle and was about to pour the boiling water onto the tea, when she collapsed – unconscious. Over two litres of boiling water poured all over her! The kitchen-maid ran for the First-Aider who put wet towels over her but the damage was done, and Mary was covered in terrible scalds.

Rushed by Ambulance to Hereford Hospital, she stayed for the weekend only and not seen by a consultant. She had huge blisters which were weeping and areas of red scalded skin. Pethidine was given for pain relief and cream applied to the scalds, then she was sent home.

She suffered 18 weeks of daily dressings which were extremely painful and after all that time was eventually admitted to the 'burns unit' of the Selly Oak Hospital in Birmingham, to treat the terrible contractures and scars. She underwent three skin-graft operations over the following months. Friends recommended that Mary had grounds for taking legal advice about suing the Health Authority for negligence.

The head of the Burns Unit at Selly Oak recommended suing the Hereford Trust and the Worcester Trust. After three years and many investigations, photographs taken and evidence from many disciplines, no sympathy was shown but she won her case.

The following year, June 2004 Mary married Paul, the widower of her friend Pauline Kelly. Mary has continued to work when she could, in between operations, and carried on until 2006 when she retired. Several of the factories had closed down by now, including Evesham Foods, Garringtons and Kay's.

Mary and Paul spent the next few years travelling extensively, Palm Springs, Thailand, Cruising etc. Mary also plays croquet and volunteers at 'Greyfriars', Huntington Hall and the Swan Theatre. She has two daughters and four grandchildren, and is a life member of the Worcester Royal Infirmary Nurses League.

A full and interesting life of the girl from Dunmanway, a life of 'highs' and 'lows' but never dull.

MARY AND NEIL ATTENDING MATRON'S BALL AT THE GUILDHALL 1955

THE MAIDS

MULBERRY HOUSE was where the maids lived in the 1950's and 1960's. It had been built as a nurse's home in 1897 when Miss Mary Herbert became Matron.

Mulberry House held 33 nurses' rooms, but by 1930 the School of Nursing had expanded so much that a much larger Nurses Home was required. This new Nurses Home was opened in 1932 by the Prince of Wales, leaving Mulberry House free to house the Maids. Many of the maids came over from Ireland, and spent the rest of their lives working as maids at the Infirmary.

There was a hierarchy of maids, for example – Matron's maid – Olive was far superior to a kitchen maid, much as you would find in a Palace or Grand House. Each ward sister had their own maid attached to the ward, and it was her most important job to keep the ward sister happy.

She would make sure there was a plentiful supply of tea and coffee, when a Consultant came to do his rounds. She would also pop out to the shops or do any other errands for sister. She also washed up all the dishes after the patients' meals and supervised the student nurses 'damp dusting the ward'. Her other main job was to clean the ward floor every day.

From a student nurse's point of view, it was important to 'keep in' with the ward maid, as she could make your life a misery if she chose, having such a close relationship with the ward sister. The Ward Maid never seemed to have a day off, they were always there on the ward, but I suppose they must have had some time off.

The maids in the dining room were all very cheerful and friendly and would give you an extra sausage or helping of custard if you asked. We were always hungry, and I think the maids realised that we needed plenty of food, as our work was so very strenuous and tiring.

There was also a team of maids who did the cleaning of the corridors, stairs and sitting room etc., whom we didn't really come into contact with so often, although in the nurses' home there were two ladies whose sole responsibility was to make all the nurses beds, including changing all the sheets of course. We all got on well with these maids who were very popular.

A senior nurse was in charge of the maids, and she planned their duties and made a regular inspection of their work, to make sure everything was done properly.

The maids were the oil in the engine of the hospital ensuring everything worked as it should. They seemed very happy people, enjoying their important role. When the Domestic Services were sub-contracted out in the 1970's all this changed. The Maids all left, to be replaced by strangers who didn't know the Hospital or the Nurses. Mulberry House was vacated by the Maids and was then a residence for doctors.

The new people were not called Maids and were only answerable to their employers and not the nursing staff. Consequently, in my opinion, the standard of cleanliness of the Hospital went down, because the new staff were paid much lower rates. I know the Hospital had to save money, but this was a retrograde step.

Losing the control and contact between the Nursing staff and Maids broke the long tradition which had maintained such a high standard of cleanliness and co-operation over many years.

The same thing happened with the catering. Regarded by the Nurses such an important part of each patient's recovery, the control and distribution of all types of food including special diets, was removed to be put in the hands of 'outside caterers. To make matters worse, I believe the food came from Manchester! How on earth can they know what Mrs. Smith on Wheeley Lea feels like today and what she would like for her lunch? This system has resulted in chaotic meal-times, overseen by non-nursing staff who don't have a clue what is wrong with any of the patients. Resulting in many patients not receiving their correct diet. Is this progress I wonder?

MULBERRY HOUSE

HOSPITAL FOOD

I can see you now, wrinkling your nose thinking, what can I possibly write about this subject? Well of course the patients and staff were all captive customers who had no choice at all but relied on Hospital Food as we all lived on the premises.

The large kitchens cooked good wholesome English Food – roast joints of meat on Sundays, followed by sponge puddings and custard. Then the dripping from the meat was served up with bread for morning break on the following days – we loved it!

The patients and staff mostly had the same food except for special diets of course. The ward Sister would give out the meals, served from a hot trolley, which had been sent up from the kitchen, making sure each patient received food to his liking and appetite, allocating a nurse to help feed those patients unable to feed themselves. It was considered very important that patients received nourishing, tasty food. For one period the head chef was an ex-army chef who prided himself on producing good food and would tour the wards later in the day to ask patients opinions on the standard of the food.

A HOSPITAL KITCHEN, GREAT NORTHERN, HOLLOWAY ROAD
1916. VERY SIMILAR TO WORCESTER.

We had a cooked breakfast every morning except Sunday when it was cold ham and grapefruit. We could only have two items, bacon and tomato or sausage and beans, or egg and fried bread, or any other combination. It was always a 'rush' to eat breakfast as we had to be on duty at 7.30am.

Sister Armstrong, the Night Superintendent would come bustling into the Dining Room at about 7.20am to call the register as it was compulsory for those going on duty to have breakfast, so most people squeezed into the dining room in time to have a mouth full of food. Then the Nurses filed out in order of seniority with new students last to leave.

Lunch was a hearty meal of stew and dumplings, or cottage pie, or some other traditional meal with a hot pudding. We were glad to have this food as we were always starving hungry and yet none of us got fat. I suppose we used up all the calories racing up and down the wards. I cannot ever remember anyone wanting to go 'on a diet' to lose weight.

At 4.00pm tea was served, with home-made cakes. The same was served to the patients on the wards and then supper at 7.30pm – macaroni cheese or salad, that kind of thing, with ice cream for pudding.

In 1954 when I started my training some foods were still 'rationed', so at the beginning of every week, usually Monday morning, each Nurse would have to report to Bryn, who had a little storeroom in the basement. Here we would be given ¼ lb of butter on a saucer and half a jam-jar of sugar. This was to last us for a week. Bryn was in charge of 'stores', and he kept a list of everything in his head. He would send biscuits and tea to the wards, toilet rolls, light bulbs and a huge range of necessary items, all crammed into this small space. It was amazing that he could find anything.

When we were on 'nights' we had our meals served in a small dining room in the basement – Breakfast at 7.30pm, Lunch or a snack at 12.30am, then Dinner at 7.30am. When you have been working all night, Fish and Chips or some other heavy meal is not welcome at 7.30am, no matter how hungry we were. I think the food was warmed-up from the night before.

One hundred years earlier, in 1861, the diet of the hospital came under review. For many years, meat had been boiled, as some committee somewhere had stated that roasting meat was wasteful. But the Doctors believed that the extra expense of roasting meat was worth it, as the meat was much more palatable and went far to improve the diet of the patients.

There was heavy consumption of wine and beer, due to the increasing number of patients requiring 'continual support'. The weekly committee members were dismayed to learn that the hospital had consumed 6,346 gallons of Ale in 12 months. It was decided that in future boys under the age of fourteen should only receive half a pint a day, while children under eight should just have milk and no Ale.

Because of the high cost of Tea, broth was substituted, much to the disgust of the patients. Many preferred to bring their own Tea which they 'brewed up' in their own 'billy-cans' at their own expense.

Patients on full diets at that time received everyday – 5 ounces of meat, 16 ounces of bread, 12 ounces of potatoes and 2 pints of Ale. 7 Ounces of butter a week was also given, so patients were fairly well fed.

A report in the same year, 1861, also states that they were not in favour of the practice of allowing more than one patient in each bed! Great skill was required by the House Surgeons in selecting occupants for certain beds!

CHRISTMAS IN HOSPITAL – 1954

The thought of having to spend Christmas in hospital is obviously quite daunting to most patients, so therefore the nurses go to great lengths to make the day as enjoyable as possible. As many patients as is safe are sent home the day before.

The preparations start on Christmas Eve when the decorations are taken out of the cupboard and hung around the ward, the beds and windows strung with tinsel in many colours, and a large tree put up in the corner, with flashing lights and a star on the top. There is usually a Centre piece made of cotton wool – a snow scene or Disney characters, each ward competing to have the best display.

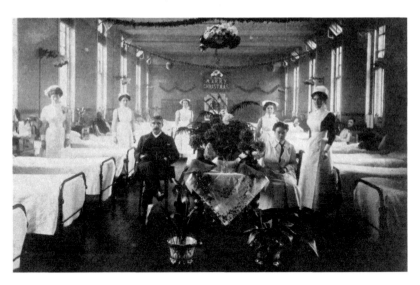

CHRISTMAS ON THE WARD

Christmas was a time when the kitchens excelled themselves, producing the most amazing spread of Turkey, trifles, cakes, puddings, sausages and hams. The wards would be decorated on Christmas Eve, then the nurses would sing carols dressed in uniform, with their capes with the red lining on the outside, carrying lanterns. Then all the food would be brought up to the wards on Christmas morning. Usually the ward Sisters had saved some money to buy bottles of sherry and wine, which surprisingly was not banned. Patients and Nurses were allowed a glass or two. I remember the Mayor touring the wards accompanied by various VIP's including Carys Elgar. One patient grabbed hold of the Mayor and said, "They are poisoning me", because he had had a glass of wine!

Menu

Iced melon
Or
Cream of Tomato Soup
✫

Roast Turkey and Boiled ham
Chipolata Sausages
Bread Sauce
Brussels Sprouts
Roast and Boiled Potatoes
✫

Christmas Pudding and Rum Sauce
Rum Butter - Mince Pies
Trifle
✫

Cheese and Biscuits
✫

Dessert

CHRISTMAS MENU - THURSDAY, 28TH DECEMBER 1972

Father Christmas would then come round with his sack of presents and then the Turkey with all the trimmings came up from the kitchen. One of the Consultant Surgeons would then carve the Turkey, to the great amusement of the patients, but it had become a tradition, crackers, with fancy hats a glass of wine and a generous helping of Christmas pudding completed the meal. The Patient's relatives would arrive in the afternoon to join in the festivities.

On the children's wards, great excitement ensues as Father Christmas arrives with his sack of toys, and a gift for each child, he then goes on to the other wards delivering presents for all the patients.

The Nurses all worked all Christmas day to give the patients unfortunate enough to have to stay in hospital a lovely time. We had usually cold ham, rice and beetroot – and then Boxing Day we would have our Christmas Dinner, served by the Doctors. Then we would all go to watch the Christmas Concert in the Recreation Room.

One of the other traditions was on Christmas morning the Salvation Army would play carols in the courtyard in front of the hospital. It was such a very happy time for us all that none of as wanted to have the day off and miss all the fun. You see there were very few married nurses. The students 'lived-in' and so did most of the Sisters, so their lives were centred on the Hospital and all its activities.

In the Operating Theatre the staff would provide refreshments for all the Consultants who brought their families to visit and then we would cook our Turkey in the tiny kitchen. John Smith, the Senior Charge Nurse was always in charge of the cooking. With the meal we had a glass of pink Champagne. One Theatre always had to be ready in case of emergencies of course, and we kept our fingers crossed that no-one would need surgery while we were eating our dinner.

The Hospital was buzzing with happy people all day long, and I do believe that many patients spent a much happier day than they had anticipated, and maybe some lonely people who usually spent the day on their own really had a great time.

CHRISTMAS ON WARD 12 RONKSWOOD 1965

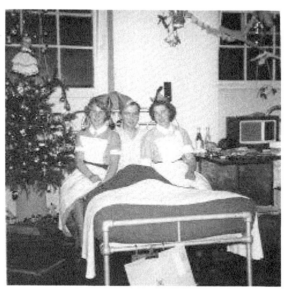

CHRISTMAS ON RUSHOUT WARD 1954. AUTHOR ON LEFT MARGOT
ELLIOTT ON RIGHT

NIGHT DUTY

Working 'Nights' was something you either loved or hated. As students we dreaded going on to nights as it meant living in the Night Nurses Home in Bath Road, a very large pair of semi-detached Victorian houses which had been converted to accommodate nurses two or three to a room. It was looked after by a Senior Home Sister, Miss Senter and a maid. We had to sleep all day from 9.00am to 6.00pm when we were woken with a cup of tea, after bathing and dressing in our uniforms we were taken by coach to the hospital, where we had breakfast and then went on duty at 8.30pm.

NIGHT NURSES HOME, BATH ROAD, WORCESTER

There were usually just two nurses per ward, one junior and one senior third year student nurse. There were always three Night Sisters on duty. They would regularly visit the wards to do their 'rounds'. The student nurse would conduct a tour of the ward naming each patient, his / her diagnosis, treatment and prognosis. Woe betide the student who was not able to give Night Sister this detailed information. The Night Sister would also check any drugs required and also deal with any problems or emergencies.

The third Night Sister would be responsible for Casualty and its organisation during the night hours. On the wards the patients were each given a hot drink, then bed-pans and pressure-areas treated, and all settled down for the night with any necessary medication given usually at 10.00pm. Lights out was as early as possible, but often if you were busy with patients needing treatment of various kinds, like dressings, it could be 11.30pm or later.

Working on surgical or orthopaedic wards meant that emergency patients would be admitted into the ward and often go to theatre for urgent operations - for example, appendicectomy. Road accident and industrial / farming accident victims would often be admitted at night, also requiring major surgery.

Often there were 'the drunks' to cope with, especially on a Saturday night in summer. The Gypsies would stay in the area fruit-picking or hop-picking and would get drunk on pay-day. They would be brought into the hospital if they had fallen and injured themselves, their pockets full of rolls of banknotes. A porter was usually sent for to sit with these noisy troublesome patients overnight.

The children's wards were quite a challenge at night. The small babies needed to be bottle-fed every three or four hours. I remember working on Bates Med' when there was a whooping-cough epidemic, literally running from one baby to another in their cubicles to stop them inhaling their vomit whilst coughing. Another time in the same ward there was an epidemic of polio, when the children became paralysed and had to be put into an Iron-lung. This was in the days before immunisation against polio and other infectious diseases had been discovered.

At the end of the night-shift all the dirty nappies had to be rinsed out. Over the previous 24 hours all the dirty terry-towelling or gauze nappies were put into a large bin full of carbolic solution, so they all needed to be rinsed out by hand, before sending to the laundry. The junior nurse usually had this unsavoury task.

We were required to wear soft-soled shoes in order to walk very quietly down the ward at night. Some restless patients would call out and disturb all the others, often causing great amusement and even chaos if they jumped out of bed and ran down the ward. The next morning sometimes they remembered nothing.

The meal-times for the nurses meant that while one was in the dining room the remaining nurse was alone. It was very creepy in the dark and many a time strange movements of shadows, creaking footsteps down the ward and unexplained 'happenings' were all put down to Tom Bates the ghost.

It was also very scary being alone and feeling great responsibility for the welfare of all the patients, especially if it was your first experience of Night-Duty. If anything was going to go wrong, it would be whilst the other nurse was at lunch.

The kitchen provided us with a cooked dinner at 12.30am which was always welcome. The Senior Nurse had to write a report on every patient recording how they slept, their condition and any changes, their treatment and medication. This information was given in the report to the ward sister when she came on duty at 7.30am.

Patients used to complain about being woken so early in the morning, but when you have twenty-eight patients to serve a cup of tea, wash, make their beds, take their TPR (temperature, pulse and respiration) give out prescribed medication at 6.00am; then another bed-pan round and pressure area treatment, means it is essential to start early in order to finish by 7.30am when the day-staff come on duty.

When we finally went off-duty at 7.30am we were very tired, but we had to eat another dinner before being taken by coach back to the Night Nurses Home in Bath Road.

We did three stretches of 'Night Duty' each of twelve weeks during our three years training. We worked 10 nights on duty then 4 off. This messed up our social life and our sleep pattern. On our 'nights off', those whose family home was far away had to stay in the Night Nurses Home. The house had wonderful views over the River Severn to the Malvern Hills, but it could be quite lonely during the day when everyone else was asleep.

Some people liked 'nights' and adjusted well, others hated it: depends on whether you are an Early Bird or a Night Owl. I think I must be the latter because I liked 'nights'.

MISS MURIEL BALLINGER – THE COUNTRY GIRL

South Bank Hospital was where Miss Ballinger came into her own. She was Matron for many years and was well loved and respected by all of the staff from Surgeon to Gardener.

Muriel Ballinger was born in 1929, one of four girls, in Pershore, a small pretty town on the river Avon in rural Worcestershire. Pershore has a lovely old Abbey and elegant Georgian buildings line the High Street. Muriel attended Pershore High School where she was a good scholar. She was a real 'country girl' and loved the local country-side, playing with her sisters and friends in the fields and on the riverside. She left school aged 14 years and dearly wanted to be a nurse and care for people, but as she could not start her training until she was 18 years old she worked in a local bakery shop and helped care for the baby of the baker's daughter in law.

Having received very good reports from her school, she did not need to sit an entrance exam, so in 1947 was able to start her Nurse's Training at Great Western Hospital in Gloucester. When she left home her Father said, "I will see you back here in two weeks", not thinking shy little Muriel would cope. But even though her first ward was male surgical, which was an eye opener and a great shock, she surprised everyone and persevered, successfully completing her training at Gloucester 3 years later. She was the last Nurse to receive the 'Great Western Badge'. On her day-off she would cycle the odd 20 miles from Gloucester to Pershore, setting off at 2.00pm to arrive home just in time to listen to 'Mrs Dales Diary' on the wireless! Eric White, a colleague at Worcester in later years, was also training at Gloucester at the same time.

Miss Ballinger commenced her Midwifery Training at Kingston – on – Thames when her hip became very painful. A congenital deformity and severe Arthritis was diagnosed. She completed her Part I and successfully passed the exam. However, she was advised not to do the Second part, so she worked in the Nursery of the Maternity Unit caring for the babies which she enjoyed, but eventually decided to leave, she then worked as 'Second Sister' on a Gynae ward at Hillingdon Hospital where she was very unhappy. The Sister in charge found fault with everything Miss Ballinger did or said, making life really difficult for someone as conscientious as her. So she left and came home to Pershore.

Fortunately, they needed a Relief Sister at Ronkswood Hospital in Worcester which just suited Miss Ballinger at the time. Then a male surgical ward became available where Miss Ballinger worked with

MISS BALLINGER (RIGHT) WITH KATHY MORGAN

Surgeon Mr. Hiren De, but after two years there, a female convalescent ward was set up on Ward 16 – to take patients from Henwick House which was closing down, so that was her next post.

Then; Miss Ballinger was made Night Superintendent at Ronkswood Hospital which at the time had 260 beds. This was a post she held for many years. At the time the Ambulance men were on strike and staff came to help from South Bank, which was closed temporarily. Miss Ballinger was struggling to transport a patient. Mr. Eckersley, Orthopaedic Surgeon observed how much pain she was in and arranged for her to be admitted and gave her a new hip.

Many changes were taking place due to the 'Salmon Report' which did away with Matrons and graded everyone according to their responsibilities. As this did not recognise experience, this caused great consternation amongst the nurses. It was explained that it was the job that was graded, not the person. But there were many appeals from long-serving nurses who felt they were overlooked and their expertise denied.

These changes, in my view, lowered the standards of care everywhere. Newly qualified nurses were senior to far more experienced nurses. Everyone had to apply for their own job. People were sent on courses in different and various places. Exams had been set up for 'Enrolled Nurses' at Ronkswood, a new initiative, which allowed S.E.N. nurses to convert to S.R.N.

Eventually Miss Ballinger was promoted to Assistant Matron and worked with Mrs Hartley and Miss Wade at WRI. In the meantime, the Catering Service and Domestic Cleaning had been sub-contracted out to private companies, so were no longer part of nursing duties. Not feeling very happy with all these changes Miss Ballinger applied, in the late 1960's to be Matron of South Bank. She was successful, taking the place of Miss Capewell who had held the post for many years.

SOUTH BANK

South Bank was a large house in Bath Road in Worcester, built at the turn of the century, in Gothic style. When the owner Mrs Anne Wheeley Lea, of the famous 'Lea & Perrins Sauce' family died in 1916 she left the building to be used as a Nursing Home, with profit to be given to Worcester City & County Nursing Association, for the benefit of local poor and sick citizens.

The Hospital opened in 1920 and the Lady Superintendent was Miss Murphy and the Sister in charge was Miss S.E. Buddle. In 1948 it was taken into the NHS as a Convalescent Home and Private Patient Unit. The rooms were all very large, with two 4 bedded rooms on the ground floor and the same on the first floor, together with seven Private Rooms on the ground floor and one upstairs. This single room upstairs was very ornate with lovely wood panelling; this is where Sir Edward Elgar was cared for during his final illness in 1933, being looked after by Dr. Moor-Ede and Nurse Kathleen Harrison who nursed him until his death in February 1934.

The Senior Nursing Officer from WRI would come to inspect and insisted on the staff carrying out a 'fire drill'. No fire escapes, so any patients would have to be carried down winding staircases on a mattress by nurses. This caused a great deal of hilarity as you can imagine with nurses taking it in turns to be the 'patient'. There was a lift but it was tiny, much too small for a mattress, patient and nurses.

There were five part-time Night Sisters who between them covered the seven nights. As South Bank had been part of the WRI since the NHS was introduced, any short-fall of nurses was provided by WRI. In charge of Theatre was Sister Morgan assisted by auxiliaries who were trained by Miss Ballinger. The Doctors did not like anyone else except Sister Morgan to 'scrub' for them, as she was a very talented Theatre Sister. Miss Ballinger would sometimes 'run' in Theatre when needed, but did not 'scrub'. The walls and furniture were cleaned before and after each list of operations. Not fully equipped with instruments, many had to be 'borrowed' from WRI.

The Consultants who had patients at South Bank included, Mr. Black, Mr. Windsor, Mr. Smart, Mr. Shervington, Mr. Paul Houghton, Dr. Moyes, Dr. Kalinowski, Dr. Popert and Dr. Atkinson. There was no Maternity and no Emergency facilities.

The Kitchen was run by Mrs Fennel with just one helper. She cooked for all patients and staff, including the private patients. Plain good honest food. The Gardener, Mr Jelfs grew a host of vegetables, potatoes, carrots, cabbages etc., and supplied Mrs Fennel with all she needed; he had a large greenhouse in the garden, for growing tomatoes and cucumbers. No frozen food was ever used, and Mrs Fennel made cakes every day for tea. Her rock cakes were out of this world. Supplies of everything else including meat came from WRI.

Christmas was always very special, Miss Ballinger loves Christmas and wanted her staff and patients to have a lovely day. One of the large downstairs rooms was cleared and a large table was spread with Christmas fayre, including Turkeys, Puddings, Trifles etc., and a little sherry put into the Coffee. Each nurse had a half day on Christmas Day and Boxing Day to make it fair to all. Father Christmas visited in the morning laden with gifts. There was no Chapel but the Chaplain would bring Holy Communion to all who required it.

All Laundry was sent to WRI, both patients' clothes and nurses' uniforms. No one 'lived in' at that time although Miss Capewell had lived in a small house in the garden. Miss Ballinger travelled in each day from Battenhall where she had her own house, not far from South Bank.

In the 1980's there was uncertainty about the future of South bank, rumours were flying around about closure as it was considered old fashioned and ill equipped. No money was being spent on repairs, loose floor tiles were not replaced, and there was no bed-pan washer, in spite of requests. New systems coming into force, Doctors not available when needed, and it was felt that the hard work and loyalty of the excellent staff was not ever appreciated. It was all very frustrating. Miss Ballinger put in for early retirement, which was refused.

The following year she applied again; she went away on holiday and while she was away the Hospital closed; what a sad day for everyone! Miss Ballinger had gone to Frankfurt at the invitation of a family friend. At that time the Berlin Wall was still in place and the 'cold war' situation still in evidence. She returned to find the doors locked and bolted. A retirement party was held for her and she noticed the Nurses were giggling in a huddle round a beautiful iced cake. On the top of which was written "Farewell Mother". The Nurses said to her, "Didn't you know we always called you 'Mother'?" Because she was always so considerate for her Nurses' family life, and always showed great care for her staff.

STAINED GLASS WINDOWS FROM OLD SOUTH BANK, NOW
INSTALLED IN NEW SOUTH BANK BUILDING

South Bank contained several lovely old pieces of furniture, including a much admired mantel Clock and lovely fireplaces and panelling. It all mysteriously disappeared at about that time. I wonder what happened to it all. Miss Ballinger was able to rescue the lovely communion pieces which she gave to the Bates Children's Wards, determined they would not be 'taken'.

The nurses were mostly transferred to the WRI but for many years kept in touch with Miss Ballinger. She joined St. Richards Hospice when it was in Droitwich and Dr. Jerry Bulman was in charge, doing some home visiting. Being a very homely person her main interest was embroidery; she stitches Pictures, Tablecloths, Cushion covers, all kind of pieces which now adorn her home, she is also a very keen Knitter.

The WRI Nurses League Committee which included Treasurer Topsy Davies and the Vice Chairman, Marylyn Stephens persuaded Miss Ballinger to join and invited her to become President of the 'League'. She was a popular choice and felt honoured to be elected at the following AGM. She enjoyed attending the committee meetings and her opinion was always sought by her colleague committee members. She is very modest and self-deprecating, reluctant to be in the limelight.

Miss Ballinger has always been able to see the funny side of a situation, and hoots with laughter. She also sees the positive and has endeared herself to generations of nurses, whatever role she has taken, and is a great role-model for us all.

MISS BALLINGER WITH PATIENT

BEHIND THE GREEN DOOR

As you go down Castle Street in Worcester, nearing the bottom of the hill, there is an old brick wall on the left and a wooden door painted green, peeping from behind the ivy. The paint is peeling now and the sign saying, "Special Clinic" is missing.

Fifty years ago on certain days, people could be seen approaching the door, looking quickly to the left then right, and if no one was watching, would quickly slip through the door, shutting it behind them. On the other side of the door was a path leading to the Royal Infirmary, past the gymnasium and the chest clinic into the gloomy corridor leading to the 'special Clinic' or V.D. clinic as it was then known.

This clinic was quite separate from the rest of the hospital, and most people didn't realise it existed. Only married nurses were allowed to work in the clinic, as it was thought most inappropriate for a single innocent girl to be exposed to the sexual adventures of the citizens of Worcester.

There were few patients at that time, so only a small waiting room was needed. There was also a consulting room, a treatment room and a laboratory. The staff consisted of the Consultant Venereologist, Mr John Anthony, and the married nurse. Mr. Anthony saw the male patients

THE GREEN DOOR, AS IT IS NOW

with the Consultant, and the nurse (me) saw the females with the Consultant.

Much to my surprise, soon after I was married and went back to work part-time at the Infirmary, I was sent down to the 'Special Clinic' to work. It was quite an eye-opener as you can imagine, having spent the previous four years working in the Operating Theatre. Of course I would have preferred to continue working in the operating theatre, but at that time only full-time nurses were employed there, and being newly married I felt I should just work part-time, so I had to go wherever I was sent.

The patients were all very friendly (of course) sociable people, mostly suffering from gonorrhoea, which is easily treated with one large dose of penicillin. My one dread was meeting someone I knew, but thankfully it never happened; but there was a certain café in Worcester that I avoided, knowing a patient worked in the kitchen – very illogical of me I know.

The patient's confidentiality and identity were carefully protected. Their notes did not have their names on, but we had a secret code so that we were the only people with access to that information, and it worked well.

Mr Anthony was a technician who worked in the Path Lab. He was a veteran of the first world war when he served in the Royal Navy. He had albums full of old photographs of Battle Ships, which he proudly showed to everyone. Mr. Anthony was in charge of making Distilled Water for the Infirmary and Ronkswood. Vast quantities were needed in the Laboratories and Departments. This meant that the 'Still' had to be regularly examined by Customs and Excise, to make sure it was not making illicit spirits to sell to the staff or patients.

Mr. Anthony was a great help to me and taught me to make slides to examine under the microscope. The specimen had to be mounted on the slides, stained and fixed. Then under the microscope we could identify the diplococci which caused the gonorrhoea. The difficult part was persuading the patients to encourage their sexual partner to attend the clinic for treatment.

Quite often we only had two or three patients per session. So it was decided that once a month we would run a 'warts clinic' for the dermatologist. Many young people have warts on their hands, and are very self-conscious about them, so they came to have them cauterised under a local anaesthetic. Sometimes they, or their parents, would cancel the appointment saying that they had 'magicked' the wart away – If you rub the wart with raw steak, then bury the steak in the garden at mid-night at the full-moon, then the wart will disappear. Sometimes it works! So they claim.

We used to brew tea in a flask over a Bunsen burner while Mr. Anthony told us tales of his time in the Royal Navy. If the Consultant was away, I used to take the female clinic on my own – Consult, examine, diagnose and treat.

We only saw two cases of syphilis over the three years I was there. One was a mature respectable lady who had contracted the disease from her husband years previously, and the other was a boy with congenital syphilis caught in the womb.

The 'special clinic' or Clinic for S.T.D.'s now has its own building, separate from the hospital, at the top of Newtown Road, and much to my surprise they have named it the John Anthony Centre.

I think he would be amazed.

FOLLOWING IN MOTHER'S FOOTSTEPS

BY KEN CRUMP – RMN SRN

I was twenty-seven years old when I commenced my General Nurses Training on January 1st 1968. Having qualified as a Registered Mental Nurse (RMN) after three years training at Powick Mental Hospital near Worcester in 1967, I had been successful in obtaining a secondment to Worcester Royal Infirmary for 18 months General Nurses Training (this training is usually 3 years long). I was encouraged to apply for General Nurse Training by others who had followed that route, including Dick Tainton, David Bee, Alver Thomas and Les Pope.

Since qualifying as RMN, I had been the staff nurse of an 80 bed mentally ill elderly male ward. Many of these patients had spent a great proportion of their lives in Powick Mental Hospital, which was a large Victorian Institution. The ward included a Sick Bay, Incontinence Area and a Day Room.

The interview with Matron Hulme and Principal Tutor Miss Sharpe had gone well, and I was pleased to learn that during my training I would receive a Staff Nurses Salary, then expected to return to my parent Hospital at the conclusion of my training.

I will never forget that morning in January 1968 when I reported for duty at the School of Nursing at Ronkswood hospital, then a part of the Royal Infirmary. I was escorted to the classroom by the Principal Tutor Miss Sharp and introduced to the class of female students, mostly eighteen year olds. I was the only male student, although there should have been another but he failed to turn up – I often wonder what happened to him.

It was not easy being the only male, but to be fair, after an initial period I was accepted into the class and got on very well with the young student nurses. I found most of them helpful and supportive.

My great advantage was being married to a Nurse myself, since 1966, so I thought I knew what made them tick!

Until that time my only memories of the Infirmary were of being a patient, when I was a child. I had my Tonsils and Adenoids removed in the Operating Theatre, and I remember the anaesthetic being administered through a horrible rubber mask, and noticed all the surgical instruments laid out neatly on a trolley, the theatre staff all dressed in white gowns, quite scary! Post operatively I was nursed on Bates Surgical where we were fed lots of lovely ice cream!

My family connections with the Infirmary and Nursing go back many years. My Mother Alice Rooke had a long career in Nursing; she trained at Old Church Hospital, London – a major General Hospital with over 800 beds. She came from Cardiff and qualified as a State Registered Nurse in 1934, and went on to do her Midwifery at West Middlesex Hospital in 1936. She nursed in South Wales and Birmingham before coming to Worcester, where she married in 1941. Prior to her marriage she worked "on the district" at the 'Tything Nurses Institute', a well-known Worcester Nursing Service.

After her first child was born (me) she worked at the Worcester Royal Infirmary. This was when Miss Healey was Matron. After my younger brother was born in 1945 my mother returned to the WRI. Soon after this a post for a Senior Nurse at Shrub Hill on nights became vacant, my mother accepted the post and stayed there until she retired aged 65.

My cousin Barbara was a Gold Medallist and nursed in Zambia and my great Aunt Rose was an Ex-Army Nursing Sister (Officer) and an Ex-Matron of one of the Birmingham hospitals. Although these family connections with the nursing profession must have been quite prominent in my life, all I was interested in was becoming an Engine Driver, like so many other young men and more to the point, like my Grandfather! However, I failed the eye-sight test, so I turned to nursing.

My schedule of General Nurse Training was quite daunting and demanded total commitment and hard work. The "Block System" was used in the Training School, which means students work on an allocated Ward or Department under supervision for 8 weeks, then all move into the class-room for a four week 'Block' of lectures and study, with an exam at the end of each 'Block'.

The first week I spent in the School of Nursing, with an Introduction to General Nursing, the Syllabus to be followed, text books to be purchased etc. Then the following week I was sent to Ward 14 – Men's Medical at Ronkswood. I worked an 84-hour fortnight with split-shifts, it meant I could not spend many evenings at home; on this ward patients suffering from blood disorders like Leukaemia or lung and heart complaints were cared for e.g. Pneumonia, also Rheumatism and Diabetes.

Then I went into 'Block' learning the theory and practice of Medical and Surgical Nursing. We had lectures in Physiology, Practical Nursing Skills, we also had district Nursing Experience, visits to Departments of the Hospital including the Operating Theatres. Then in March I was allocated to Maddox Ward at the Infirmary in Castle Street. At that time, it was the Male Orthopaedic and Trauma Ward. Eric White was in charge of this ward. These patients were often victims of road accidents or falls when bones were fractured. Hip replacements were not common at this time.

Then we returned to the next 'Block' for study. Miss Mason, one of the Tutors, by now had taken me under her wing and was guiding me through this very difficult learning curve. I was very thankful for her help.

June 2nd and I was allocated to Rushout Ward at the Infirmary in Castle Street. This was a male surgical ward and Sister Jakeman was in charge. The surgical wards were where the patients were treated by surgical intervention to remove a faulty or diseased part of the body e.g. kidney, stomach, bowel, gall stones, breast etc. or where a tumour had developed.

In August I worked in the Operating Theatre where Sister Life was in charge and John Smith was second in command. The Operating Theatre was a completely new discipline, quite different from any other part of the Hospital, and a place you either loved or hated. There was so much to learn in such a short time.

In September I was allocated to Ward 10 at Ronkswood, a men's Medical Ward. Miss Martin in charge, was an exceptionally good teacher. Then on to Ward 9, Duggan Ward at Ronkswood.

On to the next 'Block' of study. During these 'Blocks' of Nurse Training, these periods of work are very intensive and involved many hours of study, theory and practical. We had lectures on physiology from Dr Fawnes. Also eight Consultants lectured us – Medicine from Dr Terry, Dr Atkinson & Dr Moyes. Dermatology Dr Wood. Surgery Mr Houghton & Mr Nicholas. Anaesthetics Dr Steel and Orthopaedics Mr De. Together with Bacteriology from Colin. Henderson, not forgetting Dietetics, Social Medicine and Pharmacology.

We had practical teaching lessons from the tutors, procedures and ethics. We wrote essays on all aspects of Nursing care, anatomy, physiology etc. and read numerous textbooks. I have kept all my notes and intend to leave them to the George Marshall Medical Museum.

In February I went to work on Ward 7 Ronkswood, a male surgical and Urology Ward. Then on to my last allocation which was the Casualty department (A/E) at Castle Street. I must say this was my favourite place to work although each aspect of nursing in all the many different wards and departments presents such interesting and enjoyable experiences. Medical nursing was also fascinating, although I never disliked any particular department. The thing I really disliked were 'split-shifts'- working 7.30am to 1.15pm then off till

5.00pm then work to 8.30pm. That was a very long day! And on each ward I had to work a spell on nights as well as days, which I hated as it upset my equilibrium!

In April I took my Hospital written and practical exams and in June my State Finals. I passed them all much to my great joy!

On Saturday 28th June 1969 I spent my last day on Duty on A/E at Worcester Royal Infirmary, Castle Street. I said goodbye to Sister Bullock and Nurse John Curtain. After an amazing experience, never to be forgotten, I returned to Powick Hospital to report on duty the following week as a Staff Nurse on the Male 5 Acute Admission Ward Mental Illness.

You may be interested to know that now I am retired, I volunteer as a Tour Guide at the Infirmary Museum, Castle Street, which is situated in the old 'Rushout Ward' on the ground floor now part of the University of Worcester Campus.

CONCLUSION

After obtaining my secondment I was lucky to have got a placement at the WRI which meant I could live at home, have a married life and be paid as a Staff Nurse, having the support of my wife was very important.

Learning to train and nurse in an environment dominated by females was a challenge, but one I was able to overcome and fortunately be accepted, because at that time male nurses in the general nursing field were still viewed with some apprehensions and prejudice among the staff. You may have noticed that all the wards I worked on were wards for adult male patients. During that era, it was thought inappropriate for male nurses to care for female patients, babies and children. Consequently, I was not allowed to work in these areas. Today things are very different; we now have male nurses working in all areas and even have male mid-wives!

The nursing care at WRI and Ronkswood Hospital maintained a high standard of patient care. The teaching in the School of Nursing and on the wards and departments was also of a high standard. Nursing work in all wards and departments was demanding both physically and mentally, but very rewarding. You needed to be fit, working an 84-hour fortnight. Discipline essential, being part of a team and knowing your place in that team is very important.

These experiences have proved invaluable during my Nursing career, giving me a much wider and in-depth understanding of patients and their problems. All in all, I was very glad to be able to "follow in my mother's footsteps". I would not have missed the experience for anything. Was it worth it? - YES!

Ken Crump RMN SRN
Volunteer and Tour Guide
Infirmary Museum
University of Worcester.

KEN CRUMP (CENTRE BACK ROW)

NURSES' UNIFORMS

Uniforms were not worn by nurses at all until approximately 1868. Until then nursing staff might wear a medallion bearing the name of the ward and status of the nurse.

LEFT – DRESS WORN BEFORE INTRODUCTION OF UNIFORM.
RIGHT – DISTRICT NURSE UNIFORM

When the 'Nurses Training Schools' were established, under the leadership of Florence Nightingale at St. Thomas's Hospital, nurses were then issued with uniform dresses, caps and aprons. In 1887 lectures were given to the nurses and 'Lady Pupils'. They had to pay for their training and wore stately black alpaca gowns.

St. Bartholomew's, or Bart's as it is known, is the oldest Hospital in England, being founded in 1123, with the wards named after the 'Guilds' of London, who paid for the upkeep of the Hospital.

Each Hospital designed their individual uniforms which were often very attractive, if uncomfortable and impractical to wear. At Bart's Hospital student nurses wore blue and white fine striped dresses, white stiff collar and cuffs with white aprons. Black shoes and stockings were compulsory. Caps were a white square of starched cotton, worn to cover the hair. They were starched and pleated at the back by the nurses, quite a difficult skill to acquire.

Once training was completed a silver buckle on the belt was allowed in most Hospitals. Sisters wore navy blue tailored dresses, worn with no apron. At Bart's Matron wore a very smart elegant dark grey dress. Sister Tutors and other senior nurses all wore navy dresses and no aprons.

At Guy's Hospital, another major London Training Hospital, founded in 1726, the nurses wore throughout their training, mauve and white striped dresses. Even in the 1950's these dresses had a modified bustle at the back. The dresses had a self-coloured collar, not white. The caps were like a half a tea-cosy, and had to be folded over a saucer to be shaped before they could be worn. During each year of training, stripes stitched onto the sleeves of the dress had to be earned according to the skills acquired, and ticked off in the nurse's record log. Then after four years training a mauve Petersham ribbon belt could be worn when the nurse became a 'staff nurse'. In addition, strings tied under the chin were added to the cap.

The photograph of Mrs Muriel Clayson when she was a nurse at Guy's Hospital in the 1950s shows the attractive style of the uniform, and the photograph of the nurse in the 'outdoor' uniform too. Sisters wore navy long sleeved dresses and frilly caps, and all wore grey not black stockings, which were very difficult to find in the 1950s.

MRS MURIEL CLAYSON

ALISON WATCHORN IN WRI UNIFORM

48

At Manchester Royal Infirmary, founded a little later than Worcester, the uniform was much more elegant, with the nurses all wearing pale green dresses in P.T.S. (the Preliminary Training School). Then they wore white aprons, crossing over at the back, white starched collar and cuffs once the training commenced. The students wore no stripe on their sleeve the first year, two for the second, and three for the third. On completing their training, a green Petersham belt and silver buckle was allowed, and string to the caps. All nurses wore brown 'Churches' shoes with brown stockings, with green capes with pale green lining and pale green straps. The senior nurses, as in other Hospitals, wore navy, and Matron wore a tall lace cap.

In Worcester, our uniforms were not so elaborate but nevertheless we were very proud to wear them, and loved looking smart and attractive.

Pre-nursing Students and Preliminary Training Students all wore plain white, buttoned down the front dresses. One size fits all, so usually uncomfortable. Pre-nursing Students were girls aged 16 or 17 years who were waiting to commence their training once they were 18 years old. This was the minimum age at which anyone could train. They worked in many different departments carrying out usually menial tasks.

The Preliminary Training Students (PTS) were undertaking a basic assessment, and learning anatomy, physiology, public health and hygiene. They also learned basic nursing skills like giving injections, enemas, making beds, bandaging etc. This took three months, at the end of which was an examination. Those who passed could then commence their training proper, and were let loose on the wards.

We were then issued with our first real uniforms, which consisted of 3 light grey cotton dresses, made to measure, with full skirts and short sleeves. Fourteen stiff white aprons, 5 stiff white collars, which were attached with studs to the dress. Five plain white cotton caps,

49

5 pairs of white cotton cuffs and 3 stiff white belts. We were thrilled to put on these uniforms because at last we felt like proper nurses.

Second and third year Students would add a navy Petersham ribbon belt, otherwise the same as first year. All wore black stockings and plain black shoes, with rubber soles for quietness.

After qualifying at the end of three years, passing Hospital Exams and State Exams, you became a Staff Nurse and could wear a pretty lilac dress, a silver buckle on your belt, and a lovely frilly white cap and cuffs.

This was a very flattering style and the colour lilac seemed to suit everyone. Matron wore a royal blue silk long sleeved dress with white lace collar and cuffs, no apron but a pretty lace edged cap.

Sisters wore nicely tailored long sleeved navy dresses with white frilly collars or starched stiff collar and cuffs, they could choose. Then white frilly caps, usually no apron, but a fancy silver buckle on a Petersham belt. Sister Tutors – wore dark green long sleeved dresses and no apron.

All members of the Nursing Staff were also issued with a long woollen cape, navy blue with a bright red lining, which was worn when travelling to other Hospitals, or to keep warm in the winter.

There was a rule, strictly observed, which forbade the wearing of Uniform outside the Hospital. A nurse would never wear her uniform to go shopping or to come to work. This was because of infection being brought into the Hospital. Of course this rule was easily kept because most people 'lived-in' the Nurses Home, which adjoined the Hospital.

After passing our finals, and becoming State Registered Nurses, I remember receiving a letter from the General Nursing Council saying that I was now allowed to wear the navy gabardine coat and State Registered Hat over my uniform, if I needed to wear it outside the

Hospital. The very few Male Nurses wore navy trousers and a white cotton top, similar to a dentist in style. The value of male nurses was quickly recognised. Many men had worked during the war as Medical Orderlies on the hospital ships and had valuable experience in caring for patients suffering serious trauma. So they were keen, after the war, to continue in the nursing profession and complete their full Nursing Training.

John Smith – Operating Theatre Superintendent - was one such male nurse, and was the first to work at Worcester Royal Infirmary.

Other female nurses who were experienced in caring for patients during the war, but who had no formal training or qualifications were in a difficult position. It was decided to create a new status and so these nurses became State Enrolled Nurses, meaning they could never gain promotion to Staff Nurse or Sister. They wore sky blue dresses. Later it became possible for these nurses to take a conversion course and become State Registered Nurses. Sometime later their sky blue dresses were changed to pale green.

Nursing Auxiliaries or Orderlies had no training but learned 'on the job'. They would help out in many different ways from feeding patients to washing linen. The Auxiliaries in Theatre were good at doing all the mending, and sewing missing tapes onto gowns.

In the 1970s sadly, someone somewhere decided to do away with these distinctive uniforms and made all the nurses in all the Hospitals wear the same unattractive, plain uniforms. No caps, no aprons, trousers instead of dresses and all blue. So no one knows who is who. The pride in wearing the Uniform has gone, and the loyalty to a particular Hospital has gone with it. Even the silver Worcester Badge is no longer presented on passing your finals, because the Nurses' Training takes place in the University – I believe this is also true at all the other past Training Hospitals.

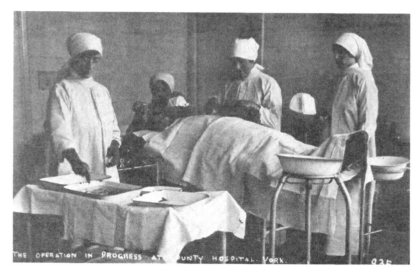

THEATRE – COUNTY HOSPITAL YORK, 1914

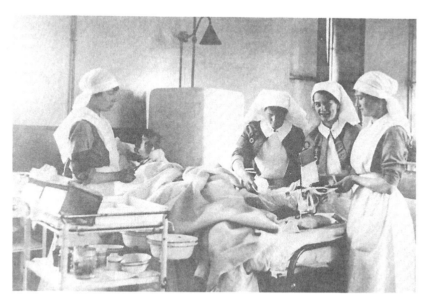

WW1 NURSES UNIFORM

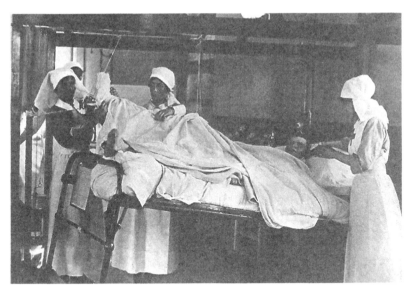

WARTIME PATIENT

PHYSIOTHERAPY

My name is Pat Wood. I joined the Physiotherapy Department when I came to Worcester newly married in 1966. Before coming to the Royal Infirmary I undertook my training at Pinderfields Hospital in Yorkshire. From there I spent two years at the Birmingham Accident Hospital in the Rehabilitation Unit. Many very severe road traffic accidents were treated here and it was excellent experience for me in my career. Following a short spell at the Southmead Hospital in Bristol I moved to Worcester in September 1966.

Castle Street Physiotherapy Department was a busy, friendly place to work. Miss Ball was the Superintendent Physiotherapist, small in stature, but with a very loud and clear voice that could be heard echoing down the corridors as she bellowed at any patient she caught not walking correctly with their crutches. She was ably assisted by her Deputy, Doris New, a very hard working and capable Senior Physiotherapist.

The Physiotherapy Department's staff covered all wards of the Hospital including the Children's Ward, also a small private ward. In the 1960's serious traumatic injuries were treated for weeks in bed, sometimes on skeletal traction. Once they were fit enough they would be mobilised on crutches, walking frames or sticks. It was vitally important that patients maintained, as far as possible, their muscle tone and joints whilst lying in bed. Ward exercise classes to music were sometimes held to assist patients to keep alert and supple. It broke up the monotony of ward life and patients seemed to enjoy it.

The Out Patients Physiotherapy Department was situated on the ground floor of the Hospital. Individual treatments for acute back and neck problems plus many other conditions were treated here using wax, electrical and other procedures. It was a very busy place with patients referred from the Casualty Department, GP's and

Orthopaedic Consultants. I was based in the Gymnasium Department with two other Physiotherapists and a Physiotherapy Helper (a very valued member of staff). The gymnasium was situated in the bowels of the hospital between the Mortuary and the Special Clinic (now called an STD clinic) an interesting position!

Our work involved the rehabilitation of patients following traumatic limb injuries and post-operative orthopaedic surgery. As well as individual patient treatments, there were knee, shoulder and ankle exercise classes. Men particularly enjoyed the knee classes bringing out their competitive instincts, especially where a ball was involved. Severe head injury cases were sometimes referred down from the wards for walking re-education and balance therapy. Before crash helmets and seat belts were made mandatory there were very many more severe head and other injuries as a result of car and motorcycle accidents.

After a break in service for a few years following the birth of my two sons I returned to Castle Street in the early 1980's to a different world. Uniforms had changed from stiff white dresses to comfortable tunics and trousers, much more sensible when treating and bending over patients. There were now more new young consultants performing new initiatives and less invasive operations. Hip, shoulder and knee replacement joints were becoming the norm. Arthroscopic operations could be done as a day case rather than a stay in Hospital which meant more patients than ever were being treated as out patients.

I retired in 2001 just before the new Royal Hospital at Ronkswood was completed and it was sad to see the old Castle Street building close its doors. Fortunately, the old Hospital is still there having been sympathetically renovated for a new life by Worcester University and it remains a fine looking building which brings back many happy memories.

Pat Wood

PHYSIOTHERAPISTS - PAT WOOD SEATED THIRD FROM LEFT

LEISURE TIME – WAS THERE ANY?

Like any young students, nursing students love to have a good time and enjoy a night out. But we were paid very little, which restricted our activities somewhat. Even if we had a boyfriend we would go 'Dutch'. No-one would knowingly go into debt; it was considered shameful, before the days of credit cards.

So we would spend most of our spare time in the Nurses Home, where regular dances were held on a Saturday night. We really looked forward to these occasions and would dress up in our finery. This was usually a dress or skirt made on the sewing machine in the little sewing room, off the student's sitting room. I remember just having one pattern, which I made up in several different types of fabric. I also recall having only one pair of 'off-duty' shoes, made of green leather, which I polished to a high gloss. During the war we could only get black or brown, so I was very fond of my Green Shoes.

We were sometimes invited to 'Scottish Country Dancing' at the Officer's Mess at Norton Barracks, with transport provided. This was good fun and I met my first boy-friend (in Worcester) whose name was Jim; he was the Regimental Dentist. He and I and the Doctor and his wife Rosemary used to go out to a local pub and drink 'scrumpy cider' – half a pint for 6d would last all evening. Girls would not venture into pubs on their own in the 50's.

One year we were invited to the 'May Ball' at Norton Barracks. Having no evening dress, I borrowed a lovely long emerald green taffeta dress from a friend. I was very small then and the top of the strapless dress gaped a bit. So I stuffed some cotton wool down the front to fill the gap!

When we arrived at Norton Barracks we found a wonderful Buffet laid out, something I had never seen before in such a colourful display. It was a very grand affair and we danced the night away. Later, looking down, I realised, much to my embarrassment, the cotton wool in the front of my dress had worked its way up and out of the dress. I dived into the 'Ladies' hoping no-one had noticed. On the way back to the Nurses Home at 5 o'clock in the morning, crammed into a car with half a dozen other people, we were stopped by the police and ordered out of the car. They were looking for the I.R.A. and had followed us from the barracks.

To go on a special 'night out' like this we had to obtain a 'late-pass'. These passes were rarely granted. So, if we were late back to the Nurses Home often the doors were locked, and without the pass to get in via the Hospital, we would have to climb in through the window of the 'sick-bay' – hoping there was no one in there who would tell tales!

There was a grand-piano in the student's sitting room which one of our group used to play. Jenny was very talented and also was often invited to parties, not only because she could play the piano – she writes, "It was in the autumn of 1957 and I had accepted an invitation to a 21st Birthday party. Another guest would chauffeur me there and back. I was living in the Nurses Home, as all students did at that time and the front door was locked at 10.00pm (or was it 10.30pm?) Special permission was needed from Matron to stay out until 11.00pm. The party didn't end until midnight, so I knew I had no chance for a 12.30 or 1am pass.

"Well I enjoyed the party; was brought back safely and found myself looking up at the high iron railings and even higher gates. Shortly, a policeman arrived on his beat and enquired as to what I was doing. He probably guessed, but I explained I needed to be the other side of the railings, and what a lovely party it had been. He must have been my fairy godfather in disguise, for the arm of the law was strong enough to hoist me high enough to clamber over. He had my grateful thanks and I wondered if it wasn't the first time he had assisted in this fashion – what perfect timing though! I managed to climb in through the sick-bay window and no-one caught me, thank goodness. Of course, these days I would be thoroughly interrogated at the local station and probably finger-printed, with the modern day need for hospital security."

Sometimes visiting stage stars or touring companies would come to the Gaumont Cinema in Worcester and send free tickets for the student nurses. One of these companies was the Carl Rosa Opera, and we went three times in a week. Dances at the Malvern Winter Gardens, Droitwich Winter Gardens and the B.B.C. Club were very popular, but expensive as we had to get there on the bus.

Matron's Ball was held once a year in the Guildhall. This was a very traditional occasion, paid for by the Hospital. We were expected to take partners, but they had to be vetted as to their suitability. So a couple of weeks prior to the Ball we had to submit the names and addresses of our proposed partners. I have no idea how they 'vetted' our boy-friends, perhaps they didn't. But we always enjoyed the event.

I suppose the favourite pastime was going to the cinema. Every week we would go to one of Worcester's three cinemas to see the latest film, usually starring heart-throbs like James Dean, James Stewart, Kirk Douglas or Marlon Brando. The only problem was we had to be back in the Nurses Home by 10.15pm - when the door was locked - thereby missing the end of the film. I met my future husband that way, when he followed us home, wondering why we left the cinema early, on so many occasions.

One year, my first year as a student, I volunteered to take part in the Christmas Concert. This was Aladdin and I was to be just a Chinese Villager, but we really enjoyed every minute. The Night Superintendent lent me a lovely Kimono to wear for the show, but I spent all evening afraid I was going to be sick over it because Dr

Piilberg had laced the drink with pure alcohol. I had to be carried off to be put to bed in disgrace. I never lived it down, and never took part in another Christmas Concert.

Living close to the racecourse and the river meant we could spend many hours just walking and enjoying the scenery. Few people took advantage of the Hard-court Tennis Courts, as not many people were 'sporty'. I think we spent enough energy dashing around the wards all day.

As first year Student Nurses in 1954 we only received £6.00 a month – which had to pay for Travel, Entertainment, Clothes, Toiletries etc., so it didn't go far. This was hard on people whose homes were far away, as they could not afford to go home very often. Several nurses came from Portugal, Germany and Ireland, so they spent all of their days-off in Worcester. If you were on Night-Duty when you had your 'Nights-off', and you could not go home, you had to stay in the Night Nurses Home in Bath Road. You always had Heinz Tomato Soup for Tea. Now, whenever I have Heinz Tomato Soup I am reminded of the 'Night Nurses Home'.

We didn't mind being poor really, as we were all in the same position and enjoyed the company of our colleagues. These friendships were very strong and lasted a lifetime in many cases. The Worcester Royal Infirmary Nurses League helps to maintain these friendships.

The 'Nurses League' was formed in 1951, over 60 years ago, by Matron Healey. She thought it would be a useful way for trainees of the Hospital to keep in touch, in the years after they left to work all over the world. There is an annual reunion of the 'League' at the old WRI (now the University of Worcester) preceded by a service of thanksgiving in the 'Jenny Lind Chapel'. This event is still very popular with approximately 100 Nurses attending and enjoying Lunch and a gossip! There is also a Newsletter sent to all members, keeping them in touch.

THE EYE HOSPITAL AND ITS STAFF

"Working at the Eye Hospital was a very happy experience," so said Eileen Cummings, née Benz, and Mary Devereaux, née O'Driscoll, who both worked there for many years.

Matron Miss Nancy Jean Hill was held in great affection and respect by all. Eileen writes, "I first met Miss Hill when I was 17 years old and, when leaving the pre-nursing 6th form at school, worked as a pre-nursing student at the Eye Hospital until May 1954, when I commenced my General SRN training at the Worcester Royal Infirmary. Miss Hill kept in touch with my progress and when I qualified as SRN invited me to go back to the Eye Hospital as a Staff Nurse working in Theatre and Out Patients. Two years later I was promoted to Sister in Out Patients, and on the Wards in the evenings."

Matron Hill was very strict but also kind to her staff. At Christmas she would give us tickets to go to the Old Theatre Royal to see an afternoon performance and on return to the Hospital would have a "Theatre Tea" for us, with delicious vol-au-vents, sandwiches and cakes that she had prepared herself.

Miss Hill was an amazing person who supervised every department in the Hospital. She was an excellent and dedicated nurse, who also

EYE HOSPITAL STAFF

acted as "Houseman" in the 1950 / 1960s as at that time there was no resident Doctor on duty. She therefore also assisted the Consultant in the Theatre. Her hobby was needlework, so she was very good at suturing wounds!

In theatre, apart from matron, there was a theatre sister, two auxiliaries and a porter. The main routine operations performed were for Cataract, Glaucoma and for Strabismus (squint) in children. Emergency surgery included retinal detachments and trauma – there were no seatbelts then! Lid surgery to repair turning in or out of eyelids.

Cataract patients stayed in for 10 days, and were washed and fed, on complete bed-rest for 3 days after surgery, and it was impressed on nursing staff to approach the patient on the side of the 'good eye' to prevent them jumping or turning their head too quickly.

The patients were very well cared for and the food very good, well supervised as there were many diabetic patients and special diets – well planned meals by the Housekeeping Sister were provided.

Miss Hill also supervised the return of everything that went to the laundry, and on Thursday mornings all the trained staff were summoned to the hall to check bed linen, staff uniforms etc. Any mending to be done was put aside for the sewing lady.

The Hospital had a nursery for the children, a male ward and female ward, 3 side wards for isolation and 1 private ward. 18 in all. In addition to Matron and an Assistant Matron there were 2 ward sisters, 1 theatre sister, 1 outpatients' sister, 1 night-sister, 1 housekeeping sister, staff nurses and enrolled nurses on the wards. The staff received discipline, good teaching and supervision.

Matron did ward rounds twice daily, she also sat in clinics with Consultants taking his clinical notes. If Out-patients Sister was worried about a casualty, Miss Hill would be the one who made decisions to admit and get the consultant to see the patient. If short staffed in the kitchen, Matron would also be there. She gave lectures to the nurses in Block at Worcester Royal Infirmary.

Miss Hill's bedroom was on the same landing as the wards for many years and she was on-call most nights. When she retired in 1966 a Houseman was appointed, and she moved into a house she had purchased some years previously. She kept in touch with former colleagues and then in the early 1970s she moved to Cumbria to be near relatives. She must have been a hard act to follow!

Thanks to Eileen Cummings for this information.

THORNELOE HOUSE

THORNELOE HOUSE

The grand Georgian House in Barbourne Road, known as 'The Eye Hospital', was built in the early 18th century by John Thorneloe, a local Gentleman. John Thorneloe was one of the original partners of the Worcester Porcelain Company. The House – named Thorneloe House, has an interesting history.

SARAH SIDDONS

In the 1760s Thorneloe House became a 'Girls School' kept by Mrs Harris and boasted among its students Sarah Kemble, who as 'Sarah Siddons' became known as probably the greatest Shakespearian actress of all time.

Sarah was born in 1755 to Roger Kemble, head of a family of 'strolling players'. They travelled around the south-west of England, stopping off to set up their temporary Theatre in any barn or Hall, as there were very few Theatres then.

In Worcester, a barn behind the 'Kings Head Pub' (later the Golden Lion) opposite the Guildhall was used. At that time, it was illegal to charge a fee for watching a play performed, so the play was free but you had to pay for the refreshment in the interval.

Sarah was only 12 when she first appeared on stage, playing the part of Rosetta in a play called 'Love in a Village'. Her talent was immediately recognised. In 1773 she married William Siddons, a fellow Actor. News of Sarah's exceptional talent spread and the famous David Garrick sent for her to go to London's Drury Lane. She proved to be an overwhelming sensation. London society was bowled over by her. Sarah's glorious reign on the nation's stage lasted for more than 30 years. She retired from the stage in 1812 and died in 1831.

Thorneloe House was later the home of Rear-admiral Francis Decimus Hastings, the brother of Sir Charles Hastings. The Rear-Admiral was the Hero of the storming of Acre in Israel in 1840. Hastings was followed at Thorneloe by Edward Evans one of the founders of the Vinegar Works, Hill Evans & Company, and of the Worcester City & County Bank.

In 1922 'Thorneloe House' was occupied by John Paul Cavanagh LRCP, LRCS Surgeon, and J. Bernard Cavanagh MB, Physician, who was an ENT Surgeon at the Worcester Infirmary. With the coming of the NHS, Ophthalmic Services were based at Thorneloe House from 1948 until 1992, when they were moved to WRI Castle Street – the building was totally unsuitable for 20th Century medicine. Thorneloe House was for the next 20 years divided up into apartments.

Finally, in December 2011, the grand old Grade II listed building was purchased by a leading Worcester Accountancy practice, the Richards Sandy Partnership, who has moved from Edgar Street, near the Cathedral. So the future looks more settled now for Thorneloe House.

CAUSE OF DEATH

Our local newspaper, 'Berrows Journal' which is the oldest newspaper in the world, founded in the 1690's, prints items of 'news' from the past 300 years – every week!

Most striking is the number of terrible deaths to children caused by fire. Open fires were a constant hazard, as there was no alternative method of heating or cooking together with people wearing flowing clothes much of the time. Children were often left unattended it seems and their clothes caught fire while cooking or tending younger siblings.

The following items have been included in reports from the past.

150 years ago – 1864

> Yesterday afternoon a sad accident happened to a child named William Pitt aged six, son of Henry Pitt of Martley. It seems that the Mother of the boy has been in the habit of going out and leaving the deceased in charge of the house and other children younger than himself and did so again yesterday. In her absence from home, the boy was at the grate when his pinafore caught fire and his clothed, with the exception of part of his trousers were all burnt. His cries attracted the attention of a neighbour named Holland who attended him, but the child died about 12 at night from injuries he had received.

150 years ago – 1864

> A child three years of age, named Mary Anne Bridges died in the Worcester Infirmary on Monday last. It appeared that about 10 o'clock on that morning, the girl was playing in the brick yard in which her Father worked. A fire had been lighted to make a stove draw, and the child is believed to have caught

her clothes on fire at it, as her Father saw her running about in flames. He extinguished them as soon as possible, but in doing so was severely burnt about the hands, but not before almost all his daughters clothing had been consumed. She was at once taken to the Infirmary where the usual remedies were applied, but she never rallied and died the same evening.

150 years ago – 1865

On Saturday last, 5-year-old Henry Best was left by his mother in bed with other children when she went out to work at 6.00am. Henry got up later in his night-dress and went down stairs to put the kettle on the fire, but in doing so his clothes caught fire and he was seriously burnt. He was taken to the Infirmary by their neighbour in Pheasant Street and seemed to be in a fair way to recovery, but complications set in and he died on Tuesday.

250 years ago

An inquest was held at the Infirmary on Wednesday on the body of John Lowe aged 44. He was engaged as an ostler at the Star Inn, Upton-upon-Severn and on Saturday afternoon last made a fire in the saddle-room and fell asleep in front of it. He awoke and found his clothes on fire and by dint of rolling put out the flames.

Later in the afternoon he was found and brought to the Infirmary. He rallied at first and every attention was paid to him but he soon relapsed and died on Monday.

Verdict – Died from being accidentally burnt.

250 years ago – 1764.

On Friday a fire broke out in the dwelling house of Mr Philip Brewer, a farmer of Norton near this City, which burnt so rapidly that with the greatest difficulty the poor man saved his wife and nine children from the flames. The youngest child being thrown out in a blanket and being much bruised.

200 years ago – 1815

An inquest was held on Thursday at the Infirmary by Mr Mence, Coroner, on the body of Thomas Shaill, the chimney sweep's boy, who was deplorable burnt while up cleaning a flue. He lingered till Wednesday at the Infirmary. Verdict – Burnt to death by the soot taking fire in the chimney he was employed in sweeping.

The Infirmary also featured in other newspaper reports

About 300 years ago – 1714.

This is to give notice that John Dale living in St. Johns, near the City of Worcester, doth scale and cleanse the blackest and yellowest teeth and make them white as ivory, and that without pain to the party. He has likewise an extraordinary water and powder which cures the scurvy of the gums and preserves the mouth, teeth and jaws from scurvy to great satisfaction. He likewise draws teeth with great ease and safety. He will wait upon Gentry or others at their houses if desired.

250 years ago – 1764

The Governors of our Infirmary at Worcester return their thanks to a person unknown who presented a complete set of surgeon's instruments last week, for the use of that charity.

250 years ago – 1764 – Cockfighting!

A 'main' of cocks will be fought at the house of Joseph Stephens at the Mason's Arms in Worcester on Tuesday, Wednesday and Thursday next between the Gentlemen of Worcestershire and the Gentlemen of Monmouthshire for Five Guineas a battle and One Hundred Guineas the main.

250 years ago

The Governors of the Infirmary at Worcester return their thanks to Mrs Newton, the executrix of the last will of Mrs Elizabeth Trebeck, late of the parish of St. Peter in this city, deceased for a Legacy of fifty pounds.

200 years ago – 1815

Sir William Smith of this County has (from a desire to serve the Charity and out of respect to the present Matron Mrs Elizabeth Brace) given directions that the Matron's room at the Worcester Infirmary shall be newly furnished and fitted up at his own expense. He has also announced his intention of leaving the furniture as an heirloom to the Infirmary.

200 years ago – 1814.

Bath Wheel Chairs – The invalids of Worcester and its vicinity are respectfully informed that they may be supplied with new, handsome and safe Bath Wheel Chairs by application to Mr Gamidge in High Street, Worcester, who has them in constant readiness on improved patent springs, for either purchase or hire.

100 years ago – 1914. Advertisement.

Nurses required at the County and City Asylum, Powick. Must be tall, strong and healthy, aged not more than 20. Previous experience not necessary. Wages commence at £19 a year rising to £25.

1984

Hospitals in Worcestershire will be places of great beauty in future, thanks to the efforts of a team of newly trained British Red Cross volunteers. They will be visiting the wards and offering beauty therapy for patients. This makes the patients feel better and that in itself aids recovery.

Before the days of 'Health & Safety' people suffered terrible accidents going about their daily lives:

150 years ago - 1864.

Thomas Anthony working at the Plough Inn stables in Silver Street, Worcester was clipping a horse belonging to Mr. Joseland. The horse kicked Mr Anthony on the right thigh, causing a compound fracture of the limb. He is an in-patient of the Infirmary where he is now going on well.

150 years ago - 1865

On Friday, Thomas Price a carpenter, was polishing a shelf in a Chemist Shop while at work. He slipped off the steps upon which he was standing and the contents of the bottle he was reaching down covered his face, neck and arms. He was taken to the Infirmary with serious burns but is progressing fair.

<u>150 years ago -1864.</u>

Crinoline Danger Again! The perils of Crinolines were illustrated in High Street, Worcester on Wednesday. A young woman trod on a piece of orange peel which lay upon the pavement and fell down. The Crinoline cage by which she was begirt was broken by the fall, and the jagged end of the broken band of steel was forced into her thigh. About an inch and a half of the steel entered the flesh, remaining embedded in it, and when the victim was examined at the Infirmary, the metal had penetrated so far that it could not be seen. It was of course extracted, and no serious consequences followed.

<u>150 years ago -1864.</u>

On Saturday last William Green a labourer, in the employ of Mr Sylvester of Hallow was attending a chaff- cutting machine, his right leg became entangled in the knives, and before the horses could be stopped, it was very badly lacerated and some important arteries were severed. He was taken to our Infirmary where every attention was paid to the sufferer, but he died yesterday.

<u>150 years ago - 1865</u>

William Hervett, aged 11, a boy living in St. Clement Street, Worcester, on Sunday was climbing a wall to retrieve a ball, when about 20 feet from the ground, fell, landing on his skull which was fractured. He was at once conveyed to the Infirmary and is going on fairly.

<u>150 years ago -1865 - SHOCKING ACCIDENT AT THE RAILWAY ENGINE WORKS</u>

Yesterday, George Lumley, age 14 years - a lad engaged at the Engine Works at Shrub Hill, was attending a planing machine when he stopped the machine for the purpose of oiling it. Whilst he was so engaged, the machine by some means got into motion and his clothes being caught he was drawn into the machine, his right arm being so dreadfully crushed that on arrival at the Infirmary it was found necessary to amputate the injured limb near the shoulder. His right thigh was also terribly hurt.

100 years ago -1914. Motor Accident!

On Friday afternoon a motor car driven by Mr A.V. Rowe, 3D, Foregate Street was proceeding down Broad Street, when, about opposite the Beauchamp hotel, an old woman named Mrs Fanny Bazward of Rectory Cottage, Dolday attempted to cross the road from Dolday to All Hallows. The right wheel of the car struck her and knocked her down. She sustained a bruised thigh and a cut on the back of her head. P.C. Collett who witnessed the accident, rendered assistance and a friend accompanied the injured women to the Infirmary, where her injuries were attended to!

100 years ago

A boy named William Gabell, three years old was walking in Little Fish Street, Worcester on Monday when a cow with a calf was being driven towards the market. The cow turned on the boy and tossed him. He sustained a cut across the forehead and was badly bruised. He was taken by pol Sgt Wilkes to the infirmary where he was treated by the house surgeon.

100 years ago - 1915

During a serious fire at a Tannery in Vincent Road, Worcester, Police Constable Holmes fell backwards into a vat containing Arsenic, being completely immersed in the fluid and swallowing a considerable amount. He was able to scramble out with assistance and all the poison was pumped out of his system at the Infirmary, where he is now recovering.

People suffering criminal attacks of all kinds were taken to the Infirmary for treatment.

250 years ago - 1765

On Friday last between six and seven o'clock in the evening, Samuel Roberts, labourer, received a dangerous stab in his breast in Angel Lane. However, he was so much intoxicated at the time he could relate no rational account how the accident happened. He was taken to our Infirmary and is now in a likely way to recovery.

250 years ago

An inquest took place on Friday last on view of the body of Mrs Grove who on the preceding evening cut her throat in a shocking manner. On Thursday she drank tea with her family and appeared sprightly and cheerful, but soon after she slipped out of the house, ran into a workshop and cut her throat with a razor she had secreted away for that purpose. She was pursued and discovered standing in a stooping posture with the fingers of her left hand in a hole she had cut in her windpipe. In her right hand she held the razor and therewith was cutting her gullet. She lived several hours afterwards to the great astonishment of all who saw her.

250 years ago -1764.

A few days since, Ann Hale was brought to our County Goal at Worcester charged by a Coroner's Inquest with the wilful murder of her male bastard child, in the parish of Eckington by strangling it soon after birth. At our Assizes on Wednesday she was convicted of murder and sentenced to death, and the following day she was executed at the County gallows. She was a well looking women, about 25 years of age and acknowledged the crime for which she suffered and behaved with great decency and penitence. Her body was afterwards removed to our Infirmary to be dissected and anatomised.

150 years ago - 1864.

A servant girl named Fanny Bannister aged 19, in the service of Mr Browning, baker and confectioner on the Tything, laid violent hands on herself. On Tuesday she had been accused of the theft of postage stamps from the shop. She made some confession of her guilt and shortly afterwards locked herself in the cellar. Two police officers forced their way into the cellar, and found the girl on her knees. She had cut her throat with a carving knife and blood was freely flowing. She was removed to the Infirmary for treatment and will be charged in the course of a few days with attempted suicide.

150 years ago -1865 - FRIGHTFUL SCENES AT AN EXECUTION

Atkinson, the Durham murderer has suffered a terrible death. When the gallows drop fell, the rope broke and the wretched man, half strangled, had to wait whilst another rope was procured. The drop fell for the second time amidst the yells of the horrified spectators.

SUBSCRIBERS

Over the centuries, until the coming of the NHS in 1948, health care was only available to the wealthy. The sick and poor depended entirely on the generosity of the more affluent Citizens in giving donations.

In the early years of the 19th century Sir William Wilberforce campaigned for the abolition of slavery. He stated that the poor are the responsibility of all citizens and he saw the passing of the Anti-slavery laws throughout the Empire in Parliament in 1833. Charles Dickins did much to highlight the suffering of the destitute in his novels, for example 'Oliver Twist'.

John Ruskin, a major figure in 19th century British artistic and intellectual life, was an outspoken critic of Victorian society, calling for a renewal of British moral and intellectual life. He gave generously to the homeless, helping Octavia Hill set up her house for the homeless scheme in London, which is still running I believe.

Octavia Hill would send out women to collect rents from these houses believing they would be able to detect any problems and sort them out. They were strict but fair and were the first 'social workers' – 'Justice through Charity'. She and some of her contemporaries said, "Individuals could and should change society".

The upper classes often felt a duty to make large donations to charities and their philanthropy was admirable in many cases. Locally the Earl of Coventry gave not only generous donations of money, but also many hours of time spent helping in the administration of the Worcester Infirmary. Likewise, in 1821 the Lords Plymouth, Beauchamp, Somers, Dudley, Lyttleton, Northwick and the Lord Bishop of Worcester all swore to give patronage and support to the Infirmary. This group were made Presidents and were given the responsibility of drawing up the rules of the Hospital for patients and staff. For example, the patients had to wash their hands and faces every morning and their feet every Saturday night.

These Presidents also had the right to recommend patients for admission, but this depended on the amount given annually. e.g. one guinea = 1 patient admitted. This was obviously a very hit and miss situation, so a system was devised in order to create a more regular and reliable income for hospitals.

A list of subscribers was drawn up and each person was asked to commit themselves to giving a set sum of money each year. This way it was possible for the hospital to assess how much money would be available each year.

In 1822 it was recorded that new subscribers' donations and legacies had been received. Donors promised an annual subscription of between one and ten Guineas each. Annual subscriptions now amounted to £1,250 and the total revenue was £2,454. Extra income came from charging victims of accidents 7s.6p a week – board and lodgings. Disbursements included £46.7s.10d for 8,352 Leeches and £14.17s 6d for Earthenware, Coffins and wooden legs.

There were now 75 occupied beds. In 1841, in order to raise more money, the First Anniversary sermon was preached by the Rev Thomas Leigh Claughton. Churches in Worcestershire gave money and the Anglican clergy would give individually. By the turn of the century there were 700 subscribers – many of whom gave to several charities.

Business subscribers had a vested interest as they needed sick employees to be cured and return to work. Some companies like Royal Worcester Porcelain ran their own "sick clubs" which paid their workers' medical bills, or compensation if the patient died or was permanently unable to work through illness. 42% of the Worcester companies contributed to the Hospital. Mutual Benefit Societies, Odd Fellows, The Co-op Society and Order of Foresters all contributed.

These annual contributions just about kept the hospital ticking over, but for any extra expenditure like extending the premises or providing more services, then special appeals had to be made to the public, who usually responded generously.

Lectures, Concerts, Balls and Picnics all raised money for the Hospital and many committees were set up in the City to organise these events. Mr Dyson Perrins, grandson of the founder of Lea & Perrins Worcestershire Sauce, was Trustee of the Hospital Management Committee.   Sales of Work, Fêtes, raffles, Bazaars etc., were necessary to provide the sick and poor with the treatment they required. Without the hard work and dedication of all these people our dear old Worcester Infirmary could not have survived.

THE STATUTES OF THE WORCESTER INFIRMARY 1836

One hundred and twenty-seven rules for the running of the Infirmary were drawn up by the committee, which consisted of 9 Presidents, 45 Vice Presidents, (who had donated 50 guineas per annum) and 6 Trustees.

The 'rules' covered all aspects of the organisation and included staff and patients. The following are examples of the rules:

Anyone subscribing more than one, but less than twenty guineas be Governors and may attend meetings.

Persons recommended by a subscriber may be admitted, only on Saturdays.

In cases of fractures or other sudden accident patients may be admitted without a letter of recommendation.

Every patient discharged or cured be furnished with a letter of thanks which he must give to the subscriber who recommended him.

No domestic servant of a subscriber shall be treated at the Infirmary except such person be incapable of continuing in service.

No woman, big with child, no children under 7 years of age (except in particular cases where it may become necessary to perform one of the capital operations), no persons disordered in their senses, no persons suspected of having the pox or itch or other infectious distemper be admitted.

No one who is considered incurable or dying, no one who has venereal disease. None of these should be admitted to the Infirmary on any account whatever.

That not more than six men and four women be admitted as patients afflicted with ulcerated legs.

One bed should always remain vacant for reception of any poor person who, from broken limbs, or other dreadful accident, may stand in need of immediate assistance.

That no Private Soldier be admitted as an in-patient until his Officer has deposited one guinea.

There shall be three Surgeons and three Physicians on the staff.

No 'capital operation' to ever be undertaken without previous consultation between all Physicians and Surgeons.

No person can be eligible for either of the offices of Physician or Surgeon, till he shall have resided at least one year within the City.

The House Surgeon shall also take responsibility as Apothecary and take care of Drugs, Medicines and Utensils in the Dispensary and of the Surgeons Instruments, and take care of the Leeches – recording the numbers used.

He should fix a ticket over each patient's bed, on his or her admission, specifying the name of the patient together with that of the Physician or Surgeon under who's care he be placed; also date of admission.

He must keep a record of all treatments and state of each patient, order for Instruments, Drugs, Spirits of Wine, Brandy or Ale.

That he never be absent from the Infirmary at the time when needed. He must be home by 10 o'clock, and any time when he does go out, he leaves notice with Matron or the Porter where he may be found if needed.

That he may be permitted to take one apprentice for whose behaviour the House Surgeon shall be responsible. The Apprenticeship shall extend to not less than five nor more than seven years.

The Apprentice shall be provided with board, washing and lodging, and pay a premium of £300 with an addition of £20 to the House Surgeon, and a further £10 at the expiration of the first three years.

That each Physician or Surgeon be allowed to have three pupils and also introduce his son as a supernumerary.

THE SECRETARY – shall be present at all General Quarterly Meetings and all meetings of the committee. He must keep the Books and Accounts in a neat and correct manner. He must pay all Quarterly Bills and keep a record of all the Subscribers in alphabetical order.

That the Secretary shall in no case blend the Infirmary Accounts with his own private accounts.

MATRON – That she should take care of Household goods and furniture.

She should weigh and measure all provisions, she must keep a daily account of all.

She should take care that the wards, chambers, beds, clothes and linen be kept neat and clean, all patients and servants shall be submissive and obedient to her, over whom she must consider herself as the absolute and responsible Mistress.

She must keep a diet book by which the number of patients upon each diet may be known, and also a book to account for the daily consumption of Porter and Ale ordered for the use of patients. That she treat the patients with kindness and civility.

That she takes care of all the keys to the doors and see that the outer gates be locked at nine in the evening. That she appoints someone to read over the rules concerning the Nurses, Servants and Patients once a week on all the wards.

NURSES – No Nurses or Servant shall take from any patient any fee, reward or gratuity. None of the clothes of the patients be hung out of any of the windows of the Infirmary.

No foul linen to be kept on the wards. The patient's shirts, night-caps and stockings be changed once a week or oftener if necessary.

That the chamber pots be emptied as often as possible. Two or more windows on each ward to be kept constantly open. That the Nurses do not permit patients to lie down with their shoes on, and they do not allow any cooking to be done on the wards.

They shall all dine together with the other servants.

SERVANTS – shall clean the wards before seven in the morning. All servants shall be diligent in obeying the orders of the Matron. They attend the back-gate and do not permit provisions, liquor or any articles to be conveyed to the patients.

IN-PATIENTS – No Patient should sit up later than 9pm and rise by 7am. Patients do not curse or swear. No men patients to go into the women's ward, or vice versa.

No patients may play cards or dice on the wards. Patients will wash their hands and face every day and their feet on Saturday. Visitors allowed Mondays and Thursdays 2 – 5pm. Patients to never go out without permission. Those able should help with washing and ironing linen, washing and cleaning wards.

All patients if able should attend Divine Service in the Chapel every Sunday morning. No out- patients should loiter about the Infirmary gate.

This information is contained in a booklet – Statutes of the Worcester Infirmary 1836 – which is part of the Palfrey Collection held at Worcestershire Archive and Archaeology Service.

A DISASTER ON PITCHCROFT

The 7th of January 1824 was a day to remember. Pitchcroft, the racecourse in Worcester was flooded. The water rose steadily but in spite of this the long awaited event went ahead. A contest and display of pugilism (boxing) had been planned between Spring and Langan, famous boxers of the day.

No fewer than thirty thousand persons are thought to have witnessed this famous fight – nearly double the population of Worcester at the time. An amphitheatre to hold more than five thousand spectators was constructed for the occasion. In addition, many emergency grandstands were erected and the masts of vessels on the river were overloaded with excited people.

Herbert Cole, apothecary surgeon of the Worcester Infirmary attended the event, but if he should be needed in an emergency explained to the Porter exactly where he could be found.

Meanwhile the beautiful coach and four of Colonel Berkeley with postilions dressed on red, pranced into Worcester. Inside sat mighty Tom Spring, proud and confident. Colonel Berkeley was to act as Umpire. It was sometime before the huge Irishman Langan appeared. Everyone was waiting impatiently for the fight to begin. Langan took stage-fright when he saw the huge crowd, but was persuaded to enter the ring.

The battle began and the great brutes hammered each other with bare fists. By the 70th round they were showing signs of fatigue but the crowd's excitement remained intense. In the 84th round, after 2 hours 32 minutes, Langan was knocked down. He had to be removed by force, covered in blood. The mob was wild with excitement and they started fighting amongst themselves causing a grandstand to give way. Many injured were taken to the Infirmary.

Doctor Charles Hastings happened to be in the Infirmary at the time and he sent the Porter over to the racecourse to seek Herbert Cole. The Porter however did not go, and Herbert Cole continued to enjoy the spectacle, ignorant of the emergency situation ensuing at the Infirmary. Matron and the nurses worked with a will attending to the injured.

A letter of appreciation together with a cheque for twenty-five pounds was sent as an acknowledgement of the assistance rendered, but had to be returned when it was discovered that Herbert Cole had been guilty of neglect. In spite of this he had enjoyed his experience watching an amazing boxing contest.

BOXERS, SPRING AND LANGAN

THE EARLY 20TH CENTURY

In 1895 the One Hundred and Fiftieth Anniversary of the Infirmary was celebrated with a Dinner at the Shirehall, attended by many of the benefactors and gentry of the County, who had so generously donated not only their money but their time and devotion. On the dais with the President, Lord Coventry, was the Earl Beauchamp, Lord and Lady Hindlip, Alfred Baldwyn MP, The Dean of Worcester, Robert Berkeley and several other worthies. In the speeches the need for a new Nurses Home was stressed, but Tom Bates, the elder, reminded his audience that the Doctors would shortly be asking for an X-Ray plant.

Tom Bates was as good as his word and as the new century approached the Doctors decided that the time has come to press for an X-Ray machine. The request came from Dr T.P. Gostling who had been a surgeon at the Infirmary for 20 years; he asked also for an electric light for the operating room. The combined cost amounted to £62. 5s.10d.The machine was placed with care in the crockery stores, and the crockery was put in another room 'behind the bread'.

The installation of the new X-Ray machine in the basement was a fitting start to the twentieth century of scientific enlightenment. Few could have foreseen that the revolutionary changes in medicine would have the effect of enormously increasing the costs of hospital management.

On this primitive machine for a guinea a time (£1.1s) any outside person could have his bones photographed by a house surgeon. Many were the visitors who came to see the wonderful rays, which do so much to help the surgeons set broken bones. In the first few years Mr Frank Westrop Coomber took over the responsibility of maintaining the new X-Ray machine. He can be seen on the right in the photograph on the next page. He ran an electronics company producing sound systems. His premises were on the Tything in

Worcester and his grandson Edward Coomber still runs the company elsewhere in Worcester. It was in constant use for the next decade. A full-time Radiologist was not appointed until 1912 when Dr Henry Neville Crowe was appointed. He had an assistant in 1931 – Dr John Ingles, and Dr Anthony Vickers in 1946.

By 1910 the Hospital's first X-Ray plant was 'out of date' so a proper department was fitted up at a cost of £320 and later in 1925 upgraded yet again at a huge cost of £1,500.

In the year 1901 the income of the Infirmary was so low that a special offer to install the National Telephone, at a contracted rate of £8 per annum, had to be turned down. In fact, not for another five years, in 1906 it was agreed to install a Telephone, upon Dr Wyndham Crow's urgent recommendation. Also in this year, 1906, the governors mourned the loss of their senior subscriber, Queen Victoria. On a visit to Worcester seventy years previously as a girl of twelve, she had generously given a sum of twenty-five pounds, for the sick poor in the County Infirmary.

You might think that the investigation of the causes of diseases was an essential part of the work of the Hospital, but it was not until 1903 that the renaissance of the pathological department, which had been dormant since the days of Sir Charles Hastings, was initiated. The grand sum of £15 was voted to equip a laboratory, and the Sister of the male medical ward (Rushout) was rewarded with a sovereign a year for keeping it clean and tidy.

Physicians and Surgeons were now able to investigate the bacterial causes of diseases, but it was not until 1910 that a Pathologist - Dr Henry Neville Crowe - was appointed, although he was later replaced by Dr R.T. Slinger and Dr Mark Bates, because Dr Crowe was put in charge of the new X- Ray department.

The practice of Medicine however remained 'trial and error' and little advance had been made since the days of Dr Wall and his application

EARLY X-RAY DEPARTMENT, 1904

of 'bark' for malignant sore throat in 1751. However, for Surgeons there had been great strides forward due to the invention of anaesthetics which overcame the severe pain suffered by patients undergoing surgery, and Joseph Lister's experiments with antiseptic methods. The death rate dropped dramatically. Previously patients died from shock and loss of blood, or raging infections caused by dirty instruments, clothes, and conditions in the Hospital.

Tom Bates achieved considerable success aiming at securing asepsis for his procedures, a new idea which was the beginning of today's technique in the operating theatre, whereby everything in the operating field has been sterilised prior to the procedure.

In 1910 the Mayor of Worcester gave £10 for a special Coronation Entertainment for the new King George V to be held at the Infirmary, and a new extension for the Out-patients Department, covering over the coal-yard with a glazed roof, facing onto Castle Street. On the

11th November Bishop Yeatman Biggs performed the opening ceremony in the presence of the Earl of Coventry and the Mayor.

So the opening years of the 20th century brought about many changes, some were because of financial need; but the Hospital continued to struggle for survival through a world war and the mounting demands of modern medicine.

TOM BATES – The Elder.

The name Tom Bates is very familiar to anyone who has worked at Worcester Royal Infirmary over the last one hundred and twenty years.

Tom Bates, the Elder, born in 1844, was the patriarch of a medical dynasty whose dedication and skills were devoted to the Infirmary over the years and whose descendants remain in medical practice until the present day.

The ghost who haunted the Infirmary, particularly the Bates children's wards, was always thought to be Tom Bates, but it was never ascertained which Tom Bates it was, the Elder or Younger.

In the summer of 2014, during the 'Three Choirs Festival' held in Worcester, I was conducting a 'Tour of Worcester' – "The Homes and Haunts of Sir Edward Elgar" and the Tour concluded with Elgar being admitted as a patient to Southbank Hospital in Worcester, where he underwent an exploratory operation. One gentleman in my group stated "It was my Grandfather who operated on Elgar". Surprised, I asked what his Grandfather's name was, "Tom Bates" was the reply, "and my name is also Tom Bates, and I am also a Consultant Surgeon".

What a surprise. It was such a pleasure to meet the present Tom Bates, who has very kindly allowed me access to his family records and memorabilia. It is really thrilling for me to learn so much more about the family, and to share the information with others.

Tom Bates, the Elder was born in 1844 in the village of March in Cambridgeshire, son of Benjamin Bates, a shoe-maker, and his wife Sarah. The Census of 1851 stated that the family by then had moved to Fermor Cottage, Great Malvern, Worcestershire, only seven miles from Worcester. Tom was the younger brother by two years of David Bates, who became a famous Artist.

Tom trained at Anderson's University Medical School in Glasgow where the Chair of Surgery was Sir Joseph Lister, who pioneered Antiseptic Techniques. Until this time one of the greatest causes of death following surgery was infection. Lister showed that cleanliness combined with the use of antiseptic chemicals, like carbolic acid, either in a spray, or dressings soaked in a carbolic solution, would greatly reduce the infection rate, and so for the first time the operating theatre could be made safe. This discovery by Sir Joseph Lister probably reduced the death rate by a huge percentage. At the same time, the pioneering use of anaesthetics enabled the surgeon time to halt any haemorrhage occurring during surgery, and lessen the shock to the patient.

SIR JOSEPH LISTER

After qualifying, Tom spent some years working in Paris where he was able to witness the work of Jean–Martin Charcôt, who worked and taught at the famous Salpêtriere Hospital. His reputation as a teacher drew students from all over Europe. In 1882 Charcôt established a neurology clinic at Salpêtriere, the first of its kind in Europe.

Tom was also fortunate to "sit-in" on the work of August Nelaton, who was personal surgeon to Napoleon III. Nelaton was the first to emphasise the importance of ligating both ends of a blood vessel in haemorrhage. This seems common sense to us these days, but at the time apparently not. Nelaton also gave his name to a probe for locating a bullet and designed a self-retaining catheter.

Another notable surgeon was Valpeare, a prolific author of works on surgery, embryology, anatomy and obstetrics. He provided the first accurate description of Leukaemia.

Jules Maisonneuve was also in Paris at this time – he was notable for describing a particular type of ankle injury. This exciting time in the history of medicine must have tempted Tom to "stay-on" in Europe, but in 1868 he came back to Worcester to set up in General Practice in Shaw Street. That year he became a member of the Royal College of Surgeons.

The family had moved to number 44, Foregate Street in Worcester by then, which was next door to Doctor John Wall's house, which until 1863 was occupied by Sir Charles Hastings.

In 1879 in addition to his private general practice, Tom applied for the post of Surgeon at the Worcester Royal Infirmary. This was an honorary post as it was considered a great honour to serve as a consultant at the Infirmary. His letter of application is on the following page, together with the Testimonial that Sir Joseph Lister wrote for Tom Bates' application for the post. The knowledge and experience Tom had gained in Paris stood him in good stead for his work at the Infirmary. These new ideas he brought with him must have been a great asset to the Infirmary and to the citizens of Worcester.

He was said to be a good teacher and enjoyed the company of his juniors. Like many Doctors at that time he was cultured, spoke French and studied the classics. He was fond of Cricket and played Billiards. He frequently wrote letters to the local press, mostly humorous anecdotes, but sometimes expressing strong views on various subjects.

Tom Bates reputation as a doctor was an enviable one. He would turn out at any time of the night or day to help a patient or colleague without any thought of reward. Many poor patients were forever grateful to him for deliberately forgetting to send out his account.

He resigned on the 18th October 1909 after 30 years of service and his son Tom Bates the Younger took over.

Tom the Elder wrote this touching letter to the Committee – "If you should give me the privilege of attending, as a mere spectator, the practice of the Infirmary, your kindness will lessen the grief I feel at the official severance from my colleagues and from a charity whose goodness and welfare lie near to my heart and within whose walls I have spent some of the happiest, and some of the most anxious, hours of my life" - he was devoted to the Infirmary - who could refuse such an eloquent request? So Tom Bates the Elder never really retired.

When World War I broke out in 1914, his sons, Tom the Younger and Mark, both doctors at the Infirmary, enlisted in the Army. Tom the Elder took over their duties, working long hours.

Tom Bates, wearing his Top Hat, was a familiar figure, one which was deeply missed when in the darkest days of the war he contracted Influenza. But for three days he remained at work in spite of the fever, and blizzard-like weather. His illness lasted seven days and he died in April 1916. The new operating theatre, opened in 1932 by the Prince of Wales, and in 1951 the children's wards, were all named after Tom Bates the Elder.

TOM BATES the Younger

Tom Bates the Younger was the first – born son of Tom Bates the Elder and Alice May Davis. He was born in 1878 in Worcester where he attended the Kings School. He entered St. Bartholomew's Hospital, London, where he obtained the M.R.C.S. and L.R.C.P. diplomas in 1904 and the F.R.C.S. (England) in 1905.

After holding several appointments at Bart's he returned to Worcester in 1909 when he was appointed honorary surgeon in place of his father, who had retired that year.

He was very much like his father, in appearance and character. He also was dedicated and devoted to the cause of the Infirmary. Tom the Younger was an ardent supporter of the wellbeing and careers of the nursing staff and it was he who established the award of "The Bates Gold Medal". This medal was awarded to the nurse who not only gained top marks in all her examinations but whose conduct throughout her training was exemplary, receiving excellent reports from each ward sister. Not surprisingly this medal was not awarded every year.

During the First World War, Tom and his brother Mark, also a surgeon at the infirmary, served in the R.A.M.C. Returning to the Infirmary after the war Tom was on hand when in the autumn of 1933 Sir Edward Elgar was admitted to South Bank Hospital, complaining of back ache. It was he who had the responsibility of performing an exploratory operation and discovered an inoperable cancer of the bowel. Sadly, he was unable to save the life of Elgar, who was sent home to 'Marlbank', his Worcester home, where he was nursed by Kathleen Harrison, his private nurse from South Bank. She was with him when he died peacefully in February 1934.

Tom the Younger not only gave untiring service as a surgeon but his surgical skill and medical opinions were very highly valued by the medical practitioners in Worcester and surrounding areas. He was always present at any important committee meeting and represented the Infirmary on many associations in the district. He didn't mince words and was able to sum up the salient points at meetings in a few words.

He was a staunch and loyal friend, often generous and kind, but hated to be thanked. He often entertained friends and colleagues at his home, and loved playing bridge. He was looking forward to celebrating the 200th Anniversary of the founding of the Infirmary in 1946, but he died after a short illness in November 1943, after 33 years' service.

The ghost of Tom Bates has haunted the Infirmary for many years. No one is sure which Tom Bates it is – the Elder or Younger, but any strange happenings or apparitions are all attributed to Tom Bates. I don't know when it all started but in early 1950s there was a strong tradition already established.

One fourteen-year-old girl with Rheumatic Fever was very ill and being nursed on Bates Medical ward in a cubicle. The bed was placed on the opposite side of the cubicle from where the bell-push was. Suddenly the bell began ringing frantically in the office and all the staff ran to the cubicle if find the patient in a critical condition. Who had pressed the bell? Was it Tom Bates? Who had saved the life of the young girl? The staff said Tom Bates had been seen on the ward, and his footsteps clearly heard coming up the stone staircase from the ward below.

Because the cubicles were all made of glass, there were often strange reflections of movements in other parts of the ward, but clear footsteps have often been heard, especially in the quiet hours of the night when all the patients are asleep.

The "Bates Wards" have now been demolished, so I wonder where the restless ghost will next appear.

TOM BATES, THE YOUNGER, AND HIS WIFE GERTRUDE MAITLAND

MARK BATES

Mark Bates was the younger son of Tom Bates the Elder and was born in Worcester in 1881. Like his brother he was educated at the Kings Cathedral School in Worcester.

He won a scholarship to St. John's College, Oxford, in 1899 were he was very happy living the life of an Oxford undergraduate. Once, for a wager, he walked all the way from Oxford to Worcester – 58 miles – stopping only to bathe in a horse trough in Broadway. He reached his father's house in Foregate Street, as the St. Nicholas clock struck noon on the third day.

After graduating B.M. in 1908 at St. Bartholomew's Hospital, he held House Appointments there and at the Worcester Infirmary. He joined his father and brother in general practice in Shaw Street, Worcester, and in 1913 took his F.R.C.S. The following year he applied and was accepted for the post of Anaesthetist and Medical Pathologist at Worcester Infirmary. It must have helped to have a testimonial from H.E.G. Boyle, after whom the Anaesthetic machine was named. The Boyles Machine was in common use throughout the country until the present day.

Almost immediately after he took the post at the Infirmary the First World War broke out, so he and his brother Tom joined the R.A.M.C. Mark became Surgical Specialist to No.15 General Hospital at Alexandria and later Senior Medical Officer at Haifa. He was twice mentioned in despatches and was appointed O.B.E. in 1919 for his service to medicine.

After the war, Mark returned to Worcester where he was appointed Surgical Pathologist and in 1922, full surgeon. He held that post until 1932 when he specialised in Venereal Diseases. He then took charge of the clinic at the Infirmary.

Mark and his brother Tom were similar to their father in possessing a quiet restful nature, a cultured mind and a love of tradition. All three of them were very welcoming and hospitable. Mark was quite modest and retiring, but on occasion quite a fine orator.

He died on January 25th 1947 aged 66 years.

DAVID BATES

According to Henry Sandon, in his book "'Royal Worcester Porcelain: 1862 to the Present Day" – David Bates is now regarded as one of the country's leading watercolour and oil painters of the late nineteenth century.

David was the older brother of Tom Bates the Elder, and was born in 1842 in the village of March in Cambridgeshire. They were both sons of Benjamin Bates, a Boot and Shoe Maker.

By 1851 the family had moved to Malvern near Worcester and in 1855 David was apprenticed to the Royal Worcester Porcelain Factory, where he stayed until 1880. He became known for painting floral subjects of great quality, as on "The Beauties at the court of King Charles II" series. He left the factory to concentrate on Landscape painting, influenced by Benjamin Williams Leader, a well know Worcester Landscape artist.

During this time, he moved house several times, mostly within Worcestershire where he found inspiration for his work as a landscape artist.

He exhibited at the Royal Academy and was a member of the Watercolour Society. Several of his works can be seen in Worcester Art Gallery and at the Royal Worcester Porcelain Museum, where his 'painted fireplace' is the centrepiece in the Victorian Dining Room Display.

His son David Noel Bates inherited his father's artistic talent, becoming a fine canvas artist, and to avoid confusion changed his name to David Bates Noel.

From – Manchip R Encyclopaedia of Ceramic Artists, and Henry Sandon's "'Royal Worcester Porcelain: 1862 to the Present Day."

WORCESTER ALMSHOUSES

For many Centuries the sick, the poor and the elderly had been cared for by the monks of the many monasteries in England.

When Henry VIII dissolved the monasteries in 1536/1540 and confiscated their lands, he set in train a course of events that was to influence charitable giving for centuries. His strict enforcement of the law of Mortmain, by which corporate bodies were not entitled to own property, effectively put an end to legacies to religious foundations.

However, a new way was found to evade the feudal dues, by forming 'trusts'. The device, which had to be agreed before death, made a bequest instead to named trustees, who were to 'use' the money for the benefit of the poor. Large numbers of these benefactors chose members of the local Municipal Corporations to hold their gifts in trust in perpetuity.

A swarm of hungry and sick beggars who had been dependent on the monasteries for sustenance were set loose on the land and new charities were desperately needed to fill the gap.

In July 1566 Sir Thomas White, by an indenture, gave £2,000 to the City of Bristol, the interest annually to be given to 24 Cities and Towns in rotation, including Worcester – in perpetuity. The money was to be paid over in the Hall of the Merchant Taylor's Company – "While the World endureth".

Thomas White's generosity was echoed throughout the country with numerous legacies to the Municipal Corporations like Worcester. Sadly, the corporations were self-appointed bodies of Freemen whose mismanagement of the trust funds led to local and national enquiries into abuse; Worcester Corporation was no exception. Enquiries into the misuse of funds were carried out in Worcester in 1624 and again in 1695.

Lord Henry Brougham's Charity Commissioners (in Worcester 1827 onwards) found serious abuse, including an illegal lease to Joseph Millington, himself a Charity Trustee, who had been Mayor. He in turn had sub-let the "Artichoke Field" (in Salt Lane now Castle Street) to the Governors of the Worcester Infirmary who had already built a Hospital there. A very expensive private Act of Parliament was necessary in 1835 to unscramble the mess.

The many national and local enquiries led directly to the passing of the "Municipal Corporation Reform Act" under which, the money that remained from the charitable bequests was transferred from the old un-elected Worcester Corporation, on 24th December 1836, to this new independent body of Worcester Municipal Charity Trustees, appointed by the Lord Chancellor. The Charities were consolidated into one holding charity in 1899.

The Charities, under the management of the Six Masters were exempted – i.e. The Queen Elizabeth Almshouses, in The Tything; and since 1864, The Lea's Almshouses, in Infirmary Walk.

Queen Elizabeth 1, in 1576 appointed Six Burghers of the City, who were members of The Clothiers Company, to administrate the Almshouses in the Tything. The present Six Masters still carry out this responsibility.

In order to be eligible for a place in an Alms-house, people had to be over the age of 50, have lived in Worcester all their lives, but most importantly own no 'goods or chattels' and have no income. They must also be upright and honest citizens.

After 1834, workhouses created by the passing of the "Poor Law" provided limited medical treatment in 'sick wards'. They were effectively the first 'State Hospitals'; or for a few pence a week medical clubs provided treatment and help.

BERKELEY'S HOSPITAL

Berkeley's Hospital is a place hundreds of people pass by every day and never give it a glance. The attractive quadrangle of buildings looks lovely in the sunshine, enhanced by tubs of petunias and geraniums.

At the far end, the Chapel, quite Dutch in style, bears a full length figure of Robert Berkeley Esquire, the founder. On each side there is a terrace of small single storey houses, with the Berkeley coat of Arms over each door.

BERKELEY'S HOSPITAL, WORCESTER MUNICIPAL CHARITIES

Handsome iron gates guard the entrance from the Foregate, with quite large two storey residences, one on each side. One for the Priest and one for the Steward or Matron.

Robert Berkeley Esquire was the grandson of Judge Berkeley, a prominent member of the third richest family in the land, owning Berkeley Castle, Berkeley Square in London and many other estates including Spetchley near Worcester where he lived.

In 1692 Robert Berkeley Esquire died and in his will, dated 13th December, directed his trustees to raise the sum of £6,000 by annual sums of £400 out of rents of his manor, lands and premises. He directed "the said £6,000" to be laid out by his trustees in erecting a Hospital in or near the City of Worcester – to consist of twelve poor men and one poor woman, to be all of the City of Worcester. To be 60 years of age when admitted, and to each of them £10 per annum to be paid quarterly, and £20 per annum to a Chaplain to say prayers morning and evening and also to administer to the sick. Plus £20 per annum for the Steward.

The "inmates" were in fact paid weekly and the amount was 2s 6d until 1799, when it was increased to 3 shillings. In August 1801 this was raised to 4 shillings a week and then to 5 shillings in 1817. £2,000 was to be spent on the building and £4,000 on investing in land and property to pay for the upkeep in perpetuity, and this still does provide income.

The site chosen for the Hospital was the site of the former City "Foregate" on the corner of Shaw Street and the Foregate, and cost £322. The building was complete by 1710.

The Almshouses were very small, each one containing a range, a table and chair, a shelf, and a bed in a cupboard. There was no water supply and no light, but candles and coal were supplied. In 1965 each house was given a new kitchenette, bathroom and toilet. They managed to do this by knocking two into one, but that meant fewer inmates.

So now there are only seven inmates, the oldest of whom is 92-year-old Cyrus Pope, a hero of the Royal Navy. Many inmates came from

BERKELEY'S HOSPITAL

the local industries, for example – gloving, canals and porcelain making.

The administration of the Trust was found to be corrupt as it comprised of self–appointed Freeman and Aldermen. After many enquiries, the Municipal Corporation Reform Act was passed in 1836, whereby all the charity monies were transferred to new independent bodies of Charity Trustees appointed by the Lord Chancellor.

Since that date the charities have been handed over to the Worcester Municipal Charity Trustees. They were consolidated into one holding charity in 1899.

In 1986 a reassessment of investments resulted in moving the endowment funds out of agriculture into commercial properties with much better financial returns, so by 1994 conversion plans were agreed, although there was much opposition in trying to modernise such an important historic building. Eventually plans were approved to convert one end of the chapel into a kitchen and toilets, so that the building could be used as a meeting place for the use of City charities and organisations. The work was estimated to cost £150,000 and a full refurbishment and repair programme was carried out over the next ten years.

In 1999 the trustees welcomed Miss Juliet Berkeley, a direct descendant of the founder, to Christmas Lunch with the residents, and in 2013 she officially opened the new charity Office on the premises. Robert Berkeley's family still live in Spetchley Court near Worcester.

Kathleen Harrison, who had nursed Sir Edward Elgar until his death in 1934, was Matron of Berkeley Hospital. In the 1940s she was also responsible for other Almshouses in the Butts, Nash's Passage and Laslett's.

LASLETTS HOSPITAL

This oasis of tranquillity in Friar Street was the site of a Franciscan Friary, the original 'Grey Friars'. The Friary was turned into a Gaol after the Dissolution, and in the early 18th century was demolished and a new Gaol built. The Governor of the Gaol, Mr William Griffiths, was appointed in 1819 and held the office for nearly 50 years.

A friendly, popular man, he gave dinner parties for his friends at the prison. He had a favourite prisoner whose perfect manner and pleasant countenance awarded him the privilege of escorting the guest's home. But one night he decided not to return to the Gaol and carried off his master's silver family plate.

Mr Griffiths was dismissed and the Gaol was closed down. The building was auctioned and William Laslett bought it for £2,250 and adapted the cells to accommodate married couples. At first the residents had no allowance and lived rent free. A Trust was set up in Herefordshire to provide for them and still does to this day. In 1912 new Almshouses were built on this site in Tudor style.

William Laslett, a Solicitor of No. 50 Foregate Street, an eccentric citizen, walked round town in a Top Hat and clothes only a ragman would buy. He was a Member of Parliament and a great benefactor, although extremely penny-pinching in his personal life. He gave land for a Cemetery at Astwood Road when the City Cemetery was full.

Laslett married Maria Carr, daughter of Bishop Carr of Worcester. When the Bishop died owing £100,000 the Sheriff's Officer seized his body. Laslett paid the debt in return for the hand in marriage of the Bishop's daughter. The Almshouses are still well maintained and occupied by worthy, elderly but poor citizens.

LASLETT'S HOSPITAL

ST. OSWALD'S HOSPITAL, THE TYTHING

Legend has it that St. Oswald's Chapel was founded by St. Oswald himself in the 10th century and the Abbess was Sister Alice Flagge, who taught nursing skills to the nuns. But other perhaps more reliable evidence exists that during the time of Bishop Cantalupe, in 1237 the house became an Almonry attached to the Priory of Worcester, affording shelter to five poor men and two poor women. But in one report it is called a Leper hospital.

At the Dissolution of the monasteries the buildings were demolished. Credit for re-establishing the alms houses is given to Samuel Fell and his son Dr. John Fell, Bishop of Oxford in Charles II reign.

In 1681 Thomas Haynes erected six houses and settled £50 per annum for their upkeep. The establishment was overseen by a master appointed by the Dean and Chapter and a steward, caring for ten almsmen and one woman who were each to receive two shillings a week together with three tons of coal and a garment once every two years. The poor men to be chosen by the Mayor and two Aldermen, had to be at least 50 years of age, have possession of no land, pension or annuity or goods and chattels.

In the 18th century the Dean elected himself as master and the steward was the Chapter Clerk. It was alleged that the endowments of the Hospital were whittled away by this mismanagement until by 1824 there had to be an enquiry.

The affair created quite a considerable scandal and the Dean and Chapter pressed for the return of all funds to the charity. There followed a "Dickensian" Law Suit lasting 50 years, with huge profits to the legal profession. The income of the charity went up to almost £250,000 per annum after the case was settled.

The Almshouses were rebuilt in 1873 in the Gothic style, designed by Henry Rowe; they remain in good order.

ST OSWALD'S HOSPITAL, THE TYTHING

LEA'S ALMSHOUSES - INFIRMARY WALK

These pretty cottage mews were built in 1864 by John Wheeley Lea, one of the founding partners of Lea and Perrins – Worcestershire Sauce. The houses were built on part of Wheeley Lea land known as Wheeley's Gardens. The houses were intended for six elderly females who each received six shillings a week, with coal and clothing.

The famous Sauce partnership was founded on the 1st January 1823 at their chemist shop in Broad Street Worcester. They became extremely successful, opening branches in Kidderminster, Malvern and Cheltenham. A special item on sale was a range of medicine chests, varying in size and contents, suitable for home or travelling, fully equipped with bottles of chemicals, scales and weights, pestle and mortar, with a list of instructions. There was also a range of chests for ships' surgeons, containing surgical instruments.

With huge profits made from the sauce John Wheeley Lea and William Perrins were able to promote and support many charitable projects, especially those concerning health and education in the county. John Wheeley Lea was Mayor of Worcester in 1835, but before that in 1834 he joined a sub-committee at the Infirmary, and in 1840 was appointed Inspector of Drugs. Also that year he moved to a grand Georgian House No. 3 Lansdown Crescent, next door to his friend and partner William Perrins.

Charles, son of John Wheeley Lea, joined the Sauce Company in 1857. Like his father, Charles was generous when funding was required, scientific and educational matters in particular. He gave freely to the High School for Girls (The Alice Ottley) and the Victoria Institute.

LEA'S ALMSHOUSES, INFIRMARY WALK

Like his father, Charles gave generously to the Worcester Infirmary. In 1895 he donated £1,000 and in his will bequeathed £10,000. He also left £2,000 to the dispensary and £1,000 to Ophthalmics. In recognition of his generosity the Infirmary named a ward after him. Charles' wife Amy continued to donate to the Infirmary and to South Bank, after his death in 1898.

QUEEN ELIZABETH ALMS HOUSES, THE TYTHING

THE PLEDGE BOARDS OF ST. SWITHUN'S

The ancient Church of Saint Swithun's in Worcester is first recorded in 1126 and dedicated to the popular 9th century Bishop of Winchester.

Throughout its history the church has been closely hemmed in by buildings of all kinds, including the homes and businesses of wealthy merchants who funded the rebuilding of the church, during the period 1734 – 1735.

These same merchants had made a practise of "pledging" gifts of money and necessities to the poor of the parish for many years, and certainly since the early 17th century. These gifts have been recorded on "Pledge Boards" which were displayed on the walls of the bell tower.

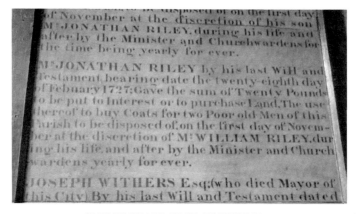

PLEDGE BOARD IN ST. SWITHUN'S

There are four boards altogether and here are a couple of the more interesting 'pledges'.

JOSEPH WITHERS Esq: (who died Mayor of this city) By his last Will and Testament dated the Twenty-ninth day of September 1741: Gave to the Church wardens of this Parish the sum of Forty Pounds, to remain as Stock for ever, and the Interest thereof to purchase four Gowns, to be given yearly on All Saints day to four Poor Widows, who frequent the Church during the time of Divine Service and Sermon. At the discretion of his Wife and Son, during their Lives, and after their several decease, by the Church wardens for the time being.

DAME ELIZABETH BOOTH, by her Deed dated Anno Dom' 1623 settled one Hundred Pounds for the use of the Poor of this City for ever whereby Five Pounds Yearly is to be paid on the 18th of October, to the Poor of this City, and it is ordered by the Mayor, and the Feoffees that Twenty-four penny loaves shall every 9th Sabbath Day be brought into this Parish Church to be distributed to the Poor accordingly.

This was two years before King Charles I came to the throne, and the earliest pledge recorded. Interestingly these pledges are not listed in date order or alphabetic order.

The boards were transferred from the old to the new church tower and can still be seen after climbing the stone spiral staircase up to the Bell-ringing chamber.

The generosity of many of the wealthy merchants and others who cared about their less fortunate neighbours must have made a huge contribution to the lives of the citizens of Worcester. The Worcester Infirmary together with many Almshouses all depended largely on this generosity.

Information from: Churches of Worcestershire, Tim Bridges.
Churches Conservation Trust.
Friends of St. Swithun's.
Photographs – Author's own.

ACKNOWLEDGEMENTS

Most of the information concerning work at the hospital are personal reminiscences or those of colleagues with whom I worked. Photographs are either the authors own, colleagues' or from the Wellcome Trust.

Mary Devereaux - The Prettiest Nurse. Mary very kindly gave me all this information during an interview in 2014, together with photographs.

Christmas on Ward 12 thanks to Doreen Cleary for photograph.

Christmas Menu - thanks to Muriel Clayson.

Miss Muriel Ballinger-very kindly gave me this information and photographs during an interview in 2014.

Southbank - photograph courtesy of Worcestershire Archive and Archaeology Service.

Following in Mothers Footsteps - thanks to Ken Crump for this account of his time at WRI. Photograph - Ken Crump.

Nurses Uniforms - thanks to Muriel Clayson, Guys Hospital, Mary Davies – Barts, & Wendy Lewis - Manchester Royal Infirmary. Photographs - Wellcome Trust & Alison Watchorn.

Physiotherapy - Pat Wood MCSP physiotherapist, kindly wrote this piece and donated the photograph.

The Eye Hospital- thanks to Eileen Cummings for the information and photographs.

Thorneloe House - thanks to Worcestershire Archive and Archaeology Service and Berrow's Worcester Journal, Mike Grundy. Photograph Author's own.

Cause of Death, Newspaper Reports, Criminal Attack, Health and Safety - all of these items are from Mike Grundy in 'Nostalgia' from the Worcester News.

Subscribers - information from MacMenemey 'A History of the Worcester Royal Infirmary' and Worcestershire Archive and Archaeology Service.

Statutes of the Worcester Infirmary 1836 - information from the Palfrey Collection held at Worcestershire Archive and Archaeology Service.

A Disaster on Pitchcroft - information from MacMenemey – 'A History of the Worcester Royal Infirmary' and from the Internet.

Early 20th Century - information from MacMenemey – 'A History of the Worcester Royal Infirmary' and from Edward Coomber who also supplied the photograph.

Tom Bates the Elder, Tom Bates the Younger, Mark Bates - all the information including letters and documents were very kindly sent to me by Mr Tom Bates, grandson of Tom Bates the Younger. I am most grateful for his generosity. Photograph of Sir Joseph Lister - Wellcome Trust.

David Bates - from Henry Sandon's Book - Royal Worcester Porcelain: 1862 to the Present Day and Manchip R – Encyclopaedia of Ceramic Artists.

Worcester Almshouses & The Benefactors - information from Berkeley's Hospital publication and the Worcester Municipal Charities Trust.

Berkeley's Hospital - information gained from personal visit and guided tour of the Hospital, thanks to the Trust for allowing me to use this information - own photographs.

Laslett's Hospital- Bill Gwilliam's 'Old Worcester: People and Places', Worcestershire Archive and Archaeology Service & Mike Grundy - Worcester News. Photograph - Author's own

St. Oswald's Hospital - information from 'Old Worcester: People and Places' by Bill Gwilliam and Mike Grundy - Worcester News. Photograph - Author's own.

Lea's Almshouses - information from MacMenemey – 'A History of the Worcester Royal Infirmary' and 'The Secret Sauce' by Brian Keogh.

The Pledge Boards of St. Swithun's - information from 'Churches of Worcestershire' by Tim Bridges, Churches Conservation Trust and The Friends of St. Swithun's. Photograph – Author's own.

THANKS - A huge thank you to Molly and John Pringle for their excellent proof - reading. Also to Roger Tapping, John Beale and the Worcestershire Industrial Archaeology and Local History Society for their technical and computer expertise, their help and encouragement. Most thanks though must go to Godfrey my husband for endless hours spent typing and patiently deciphering my spidery hand-writing, and trying to make sense of what I had written.

THE AUTHOR

THE AUTHOR, MIRIAM HARVEY AS A NEW STUDENT NURSE IN 1954

Miriam Harvey trained at Worcester Royal Infirmary 1954 – 1957 and then spent the next 40 years working in the Operating theatre, specializing in Emergency Surgery.

For 20 years she wrote Historical Articles for the Worcester Royal Infirmary Nurses League magazine, of which she was also the Editor.

Her husband Godfrey ran the Lower Wick Swimming Pool for many years and they have two daughters, both married and living in Worcester.

After retiring in 1996 Miriam trained as a Green Badge Tour Guide in Worcester where she works for "Worcester Walks" and is their Secretary.

Miriam also worked, as a volunteer, for 15 years at the Worcester Porcelain Museum.

APPENDICES

A – BENEFACTORS

The following is a list of the many, mostly prosperous people who have donated money to the poor citizens of Worcester since 1559, just a few years since the dissolution of the monasteries:

1559	KATERYN HEYWOOD - Will of 1559 - *gave* unto the Corporation of Worcester 100 marks, to be delivered to the Chamber of the said city, to the end that it might be bestowed in lands for the poor people for ever.
1559	THOMAS PRESTWOOD - 1559 - £10, to the end that the same might be bestowed in lands to and for the best benefit of the poor of the said city.
1560	ROBERT YOULE (Worcester) - Will of 1560 - **"Youle's Rents"** from 17 residential and commercial properties amounting to £47. 2s. 4d annually. These were purchased with Heywood's and Prestwood's 1559 gifts together with money of his own.
1566	SIR THOMAS WHITE (Coventry) -Indenture of 1566 - £104 from Bristol Corporation *every* 24 years, for 10 year loans of £25 to 4 poor young men, freemen clothiers preferred. His stated intention was that the gift was to continue "while the World endureth".
1604	LAWRENCE PALMER (Alcester) - Deed of 1604 - £20, to be used and employed for the best benefit of the poor of the said city for *ever*.
1604	JOHN CHAPPEL (Worcester) -1604 - £20, for buying corn for the poor.
1607	THOMAS BONNER - Will of 1607 - £40, to be lent to four young men, two freemen of the Company of Mercers, two of the Company of Clothiers, each to have £10 for three years, paying for the same yearly. Ten dozen of white bread, to be given upon Christmas Eve to the poor.
1611	ROWLAND BERKELEY (Spetchley) - Will of 1611 - £100 to be lent gratis for two years to two thriving young men exercising the trade of clothiers in Worcester.
1613	LEWIS RANDOLPH - Deed of 1613 - £80, to be lent to four clothiers, being freemen, £20 each, for the space of two years at the rate of 10s. yearly for *every* £20, which interest, amounting yearly unto 40s. was to be annually distributed to the poor; £5 each to be lent to four poor honest butchers for 2 years.
1616	GEORGE SHERIFFE (Grimley) - Will of 1616 - forty shillings, to be employed for the best use of the poor of the said city, to which Joice Sheriffe, his widow and executrix, at her decease, added forty shillings more for the same purpose.
1618	RICHARD INGLETHORPE (Worcester) - Will of 1618 - about 15 houses and commercial property in the City and County of Worcester to build and endow **Inglethorpe's Hospital** for six poor men and one poor woman and pay pensions to them. Clothiers and Brewers preferred.
1623	WILLIAM & ELIZABETH SWADDON - Deed of 1623 - £4 per annum for *ever*, issuing out of certain lands in Singleberrow, in the county of Bucks, to be distributed amongst the poor of the said city, yearly.
1623	DAME ELIZABETH BOOTH (Bath) - 1623 - £100 to be let out at 12d in the pound, to ten poor tradesmen, housekeepers, and artificers, for one whole year. The interest of which, £5, was to be given at stated periods to the poor in bread.
1624	MARY FREEMAN - (Bockleton, Worcs.) - Will of 1624 - £10, to be put out to the best use, the one half of the benefit in bread for the use of the poor people there, for ever, to begin in All Saints and so to go through the city.
1628	JOHN PALM ER - (Suckley) - Will of 1628- £120, the sum of £100 whereof (£5 a year) was to be for the maintenance of a schoolmaster in Suckley and £20 "to be laid out in corn for the poor when it was cheap, and to be kept in store, and when corn should be dear, to be sold, to the poor in the city at such moderate rates as that the said £20 might again be raised."
1636	EDMOND SIMONDS - (Hartlebury) - Deed of 1636 - £5 to be employed for the best benefit of the poor within the city of Worcester.

1636   MARY WARMSTREY (Worcester) Deed of 1636 - £10 to be employed for the best benefit of the poor within the city of Worcester.

MAURICE HILLER - date unknown - Six acres, called "Hooper's", lying in Kempley, in the county of Gloucester, the profits thereof to be, yearly, on the 1st day of November, laid out in buying necessaries and warm clothes for such and so many poor people as were not of ability to buy for themselves, as the Mayor, Aldermen and Citizens, in their discretion, should think fit.

1642   JOHN WORFIELD (Allhallows, London) - Will of 1642 - All his property in Powick, Wick, Leigh, and Bransford, for ever for and towards the maintenance and bringing up in learning of fourteen poor male children, (no bastards) whose parents are dead, or towards the maintenance of such children whose parents are of very mean ability and have not wherewith to allow maintenance unto them.

HENRY GOULSBUROUGH (Worcester) - date unknown - £40, at the best benefit that can be devised, for the raising of a yearly profit, to be bestowed betwixt three of the poorest children of the Free-school at Worcester, so as they should be hopeful to prove scholars.

1661   ALDERMAN JOHN NASH (Fryars' St) - Will of 1661 -land, property and tithes in Worcester and Powick to set up and endow Nash's Hospital for eight of the most impotent, decrepit, single poor men and 2 poor women and pay pensions to them. Three to be weavers and five of other trades.

1667   THOMAS, LORD COVENTRY - Deed of 1667 - one yearly rent of £25, from meadow-ground lying in Powick called the Great Hamme, to be paid at the Feasts of the Annunciation of the Virgin Mary and Saint Michael the Archangel, by equal portions, to inhabitants of Worcester.

NICHOLAS ARCH BOLD - date unknown - £30 for ever for the use and benefit of young beginners, and other honest citizens, and towards the relief of the poor there, and of the Hospital of Saint Oswald.

1692   ROBERT BERKELEY (Spetchley) - Deed Poll and Will of 1692 - A total of £6,000 - £2,000 to build Berkeley's Hospital, and £4,000 to buy property to endow the Hospital, for 12 poor men and one poor woman and to pay pensions to them.

1710   SAMUEL SWIFT - Will of 171 0 - £400, to be lent out, gratis, to ten honest tradesmen, such as were young beginners, and freemen of the said city, by ten equal portions, for five years.

1716   BENJAMIN THORPE (St Swithun's) - Will of 1716 - The yearly sum of £5 to be applied in buying ten coats for ten poor men of the city on All Saints Day.

1722   WILLIAM NORTON - Will of 1722 - to dispose of the interest of the £200 given to this city, to such poor prisoners in the gaol of this city, as they or the major part of them shall think proper.

1725   MICHAEL WYATT (Fryars' Street) - Will of 1725 - six houses and gardens in Fryars' Street Worcester for Wyatt's Almshouses, for six aged honest poor men, £300 to repair them and six tenements and gardens in Worcester; three in Cooken St., one in Powick-lane, one in the Broad-street, and one adjoining the Bishop of Worcester's Palace, the rents to pay for upkeep and pensions.

1734   THOMAS SHEPHEARD (Hallow) £100 on trust at an interest of five per cent per annum, for the releasing and discharging of poor prisoners for debt or gaol fees.

1789   CHARLES GEARY - Will of 1789 - Geary's Hospitals - two tenements in Taylor's Lane, called "Nash's tenements," and two tenements on land belonging to "Wyatt's Charity," "for the habitation of four poor impotent women," an annuity of £15 per annum, charged on certain premises in Pershore to pay for repairs, and interest on £300 for ever, for their fuel, maintenance, support and pensions.

1792   JOHN STEWARD (Worcester) - 1792 - £50 the interest of which was to be paid in equal proportions, annually, to the almswomen in Trinity Hospital, in the said city.

1804   LETITIA HACKETT - Will of 1804 - £140, out of the interest arising therefrom should be purchased two tons of coal, to be divided in four equal parts among the 4 poor persons residing in "Geary's Hospitals", so that each person might receive one ton of coal, instead of half a ton, the quantity then given and the residue of such interest-money, to be distributed and divided in equal weekly payments amongst the four persons to make their pension up to at least 3s per week.

Post Municipal Corporation Reform Act

1861   CHRISTOPHER HENRY HEBB (Britannia Square) - Will of 1861 - Hebb's Charity Almshouses at 18, 20, 22 and 24 South Street as an Asylum for four decayed Members of the Municipal Council, and for two poor Widows of Members of that Body. The Municipal Anniversary Gifts which took the form of redeemable tickets, distributable on the 9th of November and were of the value of seven shillings each, in tea, and sugar. Recipients were poor widows, or married women with large families.

1866   EDWARD CORLES'S CHARITY -1866 - founded by the former Secretary under which each Worcester Municipal Charities almshouse inmate receives annually five shillings' worth of "Christmas Fare."

1868   THOMAS FARLEY - Scheme of 1869 - £361 16s 2d in investments at 3% to be spent on two pensions of 2s per week to two poor deserving men, preferably Freemen residing in St Andrew's, St Alban's or All Saints.

2014   THOMAS SHEWRINGE'S CHARITY (1702) & ROBERT GOULDING'S CHARITY (1814) - Schemes originally to provide almshouses, pensions and relief in need for Worcester citizens. The joint scheme was wound up and the assets transferred to Worcester Consolidated Municipal Charity in 2014.

B – TOM BATES ARCHIVES

5

From JAMES DUNLOP, M.D., *Surgeon to the Glasgow Royal Infirmary, and to the Lock Hospital, Glasgow.*

17, Carlton Place, Glasgow,

September 5th, 1866.

Mr. Bates has been one of the most distinguished students in the School of Medicine here. His love of study, his high professional ability, his amiable and gentlemanly demeanour have won for him the esteem and respect not only of his student friends, but also of his teachers and professors. He is at present an Assistant in the Royal Infirmary of this city; one of the largest and best managed institutions in Scotland. During the last winter and this summer he has acted with great ability, prudence, and judgment as my Assistant in the Lock Hospital, where he had frequently the entire management of the cases under his charge.

JAMES DUNLOP.

From B. W. RICHARDSON, M.D., F.R.S., LL.D.

12, Hinde Street, London, W.,

February 22nd, 1876.

I have known Mr. Tom Bates for several years, and have formed a very high opinion of his professional knowledge and skill. Mr. Bates during his career as a student, won the golden opinions of all his professors. He visited the continental schools at the close of his studies, and in every way prepared himself in the most accomplished degree for the active duties of medical life. He has now been for some years in practice, and is in my opinion a candidate for the office of Surgeon to the Worcester Infirmary, who, if elected, will fill the office faithfully, ably, and successfully.

B. W. RICHARDSON.

120

From the late M. NÉLATON, *Chevalier of the Legion of Honour ; Member of the French Senate ; Surgeon to His late Majesty the Emperor Napoleon III. ; Surgeon to the Clinical Hospital, Paris.*

Je, soussigné, Chirurgien de l'Hôpital des Cliniques, et Professeur de Clinique Chirurgicale de la Faculté de Médecine de Paris, certifie que M. Tom Bates a suivi mon service et ma clinique depuis le 1ᵉʳ novembre, 1866, jusqu'au 11 mars, 1867, avec régularité.

NÉLATON.

Paris, le 17 juillet, 1867.

From the late M. VELPEAU, *Officer of the Legion of Honour ; Senior Surgeon to la Charité Hospital, Paris ; formerly Prof. of Surgical Pathology, and of Operative Surgery in the School of Medicine of Paris.*

Je, soussigné, Chirurgien de l'Hôpital de la Charité, et Professeur de Clinique Chirurgicale de la Faculté de Médecine, certifie que Monsieur Tom Bates a suivi mon service et ma clinique régulièrement pendant sept mois.

VELPEAU.

Paris, le 9 juillet, 1867.

From M. MAISONNEUVE, *Senior Surgeon to the Hôtel-Dieu, Paris.*

Je, soussigné, Chirurgien de l'Hôtel-Dieu, certifie que Monsieur Tom Bates a suivi mon service et ma clinique à l'Hôtel-Dieu, depuis le 1ᵉʳ novembre, 1866, jusqu'au 21 mai, 1867, régulièrement et assidûment.

MAISONNEUVE.

Paris, le 21 mai, 1867.

Highcliff
Lyme Regis
Dorset
26th Sept. 1879

My dear Sir,

I enclose a testimonial in accordance with your letter forwarded to this place, where I am taking a little rest before the commencement of the season.

Believe me
Sincerely yours
Joseph Lister

J. Bates Esq

13, PARK CRESCENT,
PORTLAND PLACE.

21st Oct. 1879

My dear Mr. Bates,

I beg to congratulate you on your appointment, and wish you much happiness in it.

Believe me
Sincerely yours
Joseph Lister

12 Park Crescent
Portland Place
London
26th Sept. 1879

Mr Tom Bates was a student in the Glasgow Medical School during the time when I held the Chair of Surgery in the University of that city, and he attended three courses of my clinical lectures in the Royal Infirmary.

He obtained great distinction in the classes which he attended, particularly in those of Anatomy and Surgery, and enjoyed large opportunities for practical experience both in the dissecting room and in the hospital. After completing his studentship he spent upwards of a year in extending his professional knowledge at the schools of Paris and Vienna; and he entered upon practice at Worcester twelve years ago with the well earned reputation of an able and accomplished surgeon.

His subsequent career as a practitioner is doubtless well known to the Committee of the Worcester Infirmary; but I venture to express my belief that Mr Bates is eminently qualified in the practice of surgeon to that Institution.

Joseph Lister

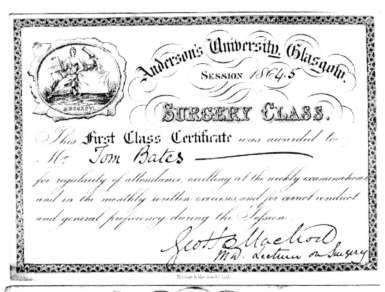

Anderson's University, Glasgow.

SESSION 1864-5

SURGERY CLASS.

This First Class Certificate was awarded to

Mr. Tom Bates

for regularity of attendance, excelling at the weekly examinations and in the monthly written exercises, and for correct conduct and general proficiency during the Session.

Geo H Macleod
M.D. Lecturer on Surgery

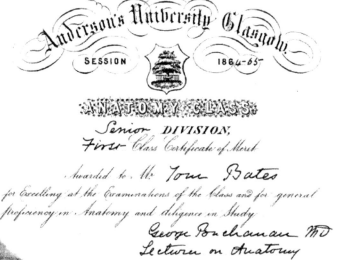

Anderson's University Glasgow.

SESSION   1864-65

ANATOMY CLASS

Senior DIVISION,
First Class Certificate of Merit

Awarded to Mr. Tom Bates
for Excelling at the Examinations of the Class and for general proficiency in Anatomy and diligence in Study.

George Buchanan M.D
Lecturer on Anatomy

124

44 Foregate Street
Worcester
Oct. 19 . 1909.

Dear Col. Stallard,

Will you please convey to
the Executive Committee of the Infirmary
my sincere thanks, for the very kind
resolution passed at yesterday's meeting with
regard to my Services, & say that I
accept with much pleasure & gratitude
the Office of Honorary Consulting Surgeon.

Please let me sincerely thank you
also for many kind acts to me on your
part as Secretary.

Believe me
Yours faithfully
F. Bates.

ST SOMETHING STREET
WORCESTER

Worcester
Nov. 10, 1909.

Dear Mr. Mayor,

I write to thank you
for being able, if able,
the meeting of the Executive
Committee of the Infirmary
at Home, on Thursday next,
the 15th inst; when the
election of a Surgeon takes
place, to fill the vacancy

caused by my resignation,
after a thirty years' tenure.
My eldest son is
one of the Candidates.
Whichever way your
vote might go, I shall deem
your presence at the
meeting an honour to.

Yours very truly,
Tom Baxter.

126

TESTIMONIALS.

From ANTHONY A. BOWLBY, C.M.G., F.R.C.S., *Surgeon to the Household of H.M. the King; Surgeon to St. Bartholomew's Hospital.*

Mr. T. Bates was formerly one of the most distinguished of our students at St. Bartholomew's Hospital, and, later on, a most competent House Surgeon. He has obtained the Fellowship of the Royal College of Surgeons of England, which is the highest surgical diploma in this Country, and he has proved himself to be a thoroughly capable and skilful surgeon. He is zealous in the performance of all duties which he undertakes, and would prove a most capable member of the Staff of the Worcester General Infirmary.

ANTHONY A. BOWLBY.

October, 1909,

24, Manchester Square, W.